DEDICATION

GRAND

MOTHER'S BOOK

OLD-FASHIONED FUN
FOR THE FAMILY

Bath · New York · Singapore · Hong Kong · Cologne · Delhi · Melbourne

This is a Parragon Publishing Book
This edition published in 2008

Parragon Publishing
Queen Street House
4 Queen Street
Bath BA1 1HE, UK

Designers: Timothy Shaner and Christopher Measom
Project Director: Alice Wong
Project Assistants: Lawrence Chesler and Nicholas Liu
Fairy Tales retold by Sara Baysinger
Activities by Jacinta O'Halloran and Alice Wong
Musical Arrangement by Frank Zuback
Finger Games illustrations by Lawrence Chesler
Recipes by Natasha Tabori Fried and Lena Tabori

Printed in Thailand.
10 9 8 7 6 5 4 3 2 1

Over the river and through the woods to Grandmother's house we go . . .

Contents

Fairy Tales

Poetry

Activities

Contents

Nursery Rhymes

Finger Games

Songs

Contents

Old-Fashioned Games

Grandmother Says

Recipes

Fear less, hope more;
Eat less, chew more;
Whine less, breathe more;
Talk less, say more;
Love more,
And all good things will be yours.

—Swedish proverb

Dance,

Little Baby

Dance, little Baby, dance up high!
Never mind, Baby, Grandma is by.

Crow and caper, caper and crow,
There, little Baby, there you go!

Up to the ceiling, down to the ground,
Backwards and forwards, round
and round;

Dance, little Baby, and Grandma will sing,
With the merry coral, ding, ding, ding!

Grandma's Glasses

Here are
Grandma's glasses,

And here is
Grandma's hat,

This is the way she
folds her hands and
lays them in her lap.

Here are
Grandpa's glasses,

Here is
Grandpa's hat,

This is the way
he folds his arms,
Just like that.

Ducklings Three

Anonymous

Flippy, and Floppy, and Flappy are three
Dear little ducklings that sail on the sea,
Sail in a tin, and a boot, and a box—
What do they care for the sharks or the rocks?
Hanky for sail and a skewer for mast,
Blown by the breezes they get along fast;
If one tips over it's nothing to him—
All little ducklings like fishes can swim.

Snow White and Rose Red

Once upon a time there was a poor widow who had two good and cheerful daughters. They were named Snow White and Rose Red, after the blooms on the two rose trees at the front of their cottage. The girls were the best of friends, and did everything together. At playtime they would run through the meadow, finding flowers for their mother, or they would frolic in the forest, gathering berries and making friends with all the woodland creatures. When it was time for their chores, they worked to keep their mother's cottage neat and tidy. On summer mornings, Rose Red made a wreath of flowers to lay by her mother's bed. On winter evenings, Snow White lit the fire and hung the brightly polished kettle to warm. The sisters would sit by the fire, holding hands, while their mother read to them.

Every night before going to bed, Snow White said, "We must always be together."

Her sister replied, "As long as we live."

Snow White and Rose Red

Their mother would add, "What one has, she must share with the other."

One evening, as they were reading by the fire, someone knocked at the door. Rose Red eagerly jumped up to answer it. But when she unbolted the door, a big, black bear nosed his way into their cottage. Rose Red was startled, and ran. Snow White took cover under her mother's bed. What they didn't know was that this was no ordinary bear. He began to speak. "Please don't be afraid," he said. "I mean you no harm. I am half-frozen, and only wish to get warm."

"Poor bear," said the mother, "lie down by the fire, but be careful not to burn your coat." Then she called, "Snow White, Rose Red, come out. The bear is our guest and our friend."

So the sisters came out, and soon grew comfortable with their new furry friend. They even made a fun routine of his nightly visits: He would come at the same time each night, and they would bring out the broom and sweep the snow from his coat. Then he would stretch out by the fire and let out a great yawn. But the sisters wouldn't let him sleep right away. They tugged his fur, rolled him about, and took turns riding on his back. He would pretend to growl and they would laugh. Sometimes, when they were too rough with the bear, he said, "Please let me live! Are you trying to beat your suitor to death?"

When the snow began to melt away, and the earliest spring flowers were popping through the soil, the bear announced to Snow White that it was time for him to go away for a while. This made her very sad, because she had grown rather fond of the bear. "I must leave you until the leaves fall from the trees," he said. "Then I will return to continue our courtship." Snow White laughed and blushed.

"But where are you going?" she asked.

"I must return to the forest to protect my treasure from the wicked dwarfs," he explained. "When the earth is frozen, they must stay underground in their caves. But in the spring, they break through to the surface and search for treasure."

They said their good-byes, and the bear trotted across the yard and was soon out of sight.

A few days later, their mother sent Snow White and Rose Red to the forest to collect firewood. They walked until they found a great tree that had fallen across a stream. Near the base of the tree, the sisters spotted something moving. As they got closer,

Snow White and Rose Red

they saw that it was an old dwarf with a long, white beard. The end of his beard was caught in the tree. "Well don't just stand there, you silly girls!" shouted the dwarf. "Help me!"

The girls were shocked to hear him speak to them that way, but they tried in vain to pull him free.

"How did you ever get yourself caught in a tree?" asked Rose Red.

"What's it to you, anyway?" snarled the dwarf.

"Well, I should go find someone to help," she said.

"Why?" asked the dwarf. "You two are already two too many for me! Can't you senseless geese think of something?"

"Don't be so impatient," said Snow White. "I have an idea." She pulled her scissors from her pocket and cut off the end of the dwarf's beard.

"You're more stupid than I thought," said the dwarf. "Cutting a piece from my fine beard will give you bad luck for a year!"

Then the dwarf grabbed a small sack filled with gold, which had been lying in the roots of the tree. He ran off with it slung over his shoulder.

So Snow White and Rose Red gathered some firewood and headed back home. They followed the stream until they saw something moving. As they came nearer, they found the dwarf jumping

Snow White and Rose Red

about like a grasshopper. "Well, don't just stand there, you foolish girls!" shouted the dwarf. "Help me! This pesky fish at the end of my line wants to pull me in. I would let him go, but the wind has gotten my beard tangled in my line."

The sisters grabbed hold of the little man and tried in vain to free his beard from the line. Snow White quickly brought out her scissors and cut the beard loose. When the dwarf saw what she had done, he screamed out, "Are you crazy? It wasn't enough that you snipped off the end of my beard. Now you had to cut the best part of it. Your bad luck will never end." Then he picked up a sack of pearls from the tall grass, and without another word, he dragged it away.

The next day, the sisters went to the town to buy needles and thread for their mother. They soon noticed a large bird circling high above their heads. The bird swooped down, and they heard a loud cry. The girls ran over and saw that the eagle held their old acquaintance the dwarf in its talons, and was trying to carry him off.

Snow White and Rose Red

They took hold of him and pulled against the eagle so that it finally let go of its prey. "Couldn't you have been more careful?" cried the dwarf. "You practically pulled my coat apart, you clumsy creatures!" Then he grabbed a sack full of valuable stones and crept under a rock and into his cave. The sisters, who were used to his thanklessness, continued on to town.

On their way home, they surprised the dwarf, who had emptied his bag of gems out onto the road. The sun lit up the brilliant stones, and they glittered and sparkled so beautifully that the girls stood still and stared at them. "Get away from here, you dreadful beings!" the dwarf said in a rage.

Suddenly, a loud growling came from the forest, and a black bear came trotting toward them. The terrified dwarf leaped up and ran, but he could not reach his cave in time. He cried out, "Dear Mister Bear, please spare my life. I will give you all these beautiful jewels. You don't want to eat me, anyway. Take these two tasty girls instead." The bear gave the wicked creature a single strike with his paw, and he did not move again.

Snow White and Rose Red

The sisters started to run, but the bear called to them, "Snow White and Rose Red, don't be afraid." They recognized their friend's voice and turned to see that his bearskin had disappeared. Standing in the bear's place was a handsome man, clothed all in gold. "I am a king's son," he said, "and that wicked dwarf, who stole my treasures, put a curse on me. I have had to live the forest as a wild bear until I was freed by his death. Now he has received his fair reward."

The prince took Snow White to his kingdom, where he married her, and Rose Red married his brother. They shared the great treasure that the dwarf had collected in his cave. Their mother lived peacefully and happily with her children for many years. She brought the two rose trees with her, and they stood before her window. Every year, they produced the most beautiful roses—white and red. ✦

The Sweetie Shop
by Jessie Pope

There are all sorts of shops
    In our little town:
One sells us nice cakes,
    Kept by old Mrs. Brown;
One sells us new frocks,
    When for Sunday we're dressed—
But the shop that sells sweeties
    We all like the best!

That's the shop where we go
    When we each have a penny,
But we stand round the window
    If we haven't any.

There are sweets in the bottles,
    And more on the shelves,
And we each choose the kind
    We like best for ourselves.

I'm fondest of toffees,
    But Jack prefers choc,
And Joan loves those sticks
    Of bright-colored rock.
We rush there with pennies
    Before it's too late,
And the shopkeeper gives us
    Extremely good weight!

The Big Rock Candy Mountain

In the big rock can - dy moun - tains, there's a

land that's fair and bright, where the

hand - outs grow on bush - es And you

sleep out ev - 'ry night, Where the

box - cars are all emp - ty And the

The Big Rock Candy Mountain

sun   shines   ev - 'ry   day,   Oh,   I'm

bound   to   go   where there   ain't   no   snow,   Where the

rain   don't   fall   and the   wind   don't   blow,   In   the

big   rock   can - dy   moun - tains.

Chorus

Oh,   the   buz - zin'   of   the   bees   in   the

The Big Rock Candy Mountain

pep - per - mint trees 'Round the so - da wa - ter

foun - tains, Where the lem - on - ade springs and the

blue - bird sings in the big rock can - dy moun-tains.

2. In the Big Rock Candy Mountains,
   You never change your socks,
   And little streams of lemonade
   Come a-tricklin' down the rocks,
   The hobos there are friendly
   And their fires all burn bright,
   There's a lake of stew and soda, too,
   You can paddle all around 'em in a big canoe
   In the Big Rock Candy Mountains.

   Chorus

Ice Cream!

"**I** scream, you scream, we all scream for ice cream!" Sundaes, sandwiches, shakes, and sodas (sprinkles and whipped cream too)—grandchildren can have it all at Grandmother's house. Indulge little ones with these treats, and they will be clamoring to visit all the time.

BANANA SPLIT

1 banana
3 scoops favorite ice cream flavors
   (traditionally chocolate, vanilla,
   and strawberry)
1/2 cup chocolate fudge sauce
1 cup whipped cream *(see page 35)*
2 tablespoons chopped walnuts
1 maraschino cherry

1. Peel banana and slice it lengthwise. Place banana halves flat side up in the bottom of dish.

2. Add ice cream side by side on top of banana. Cover in chocolate sauce.

3. Garnish with whipped cream, nuts, and finally, the cherry on top!

Serves two or three.

HOT FUDGE SUNDAE

2 scoops of ice cream
1/2 cup chocolate fudge sauce
1/2 cup whipped cream *(see page 35)*
1 tablespoon chopped walnuts
1 maraschino cherry

1. Place two scoops of ice cream in deep bowl.

2. Layer fudge sauce, whipped cream, nuts and cherry on top. Serve immediately!

Serves one.

Ice Cream!

ICE-CREAM SANDWICHES

2 dozen chocolate-chip cookies
  (see page 199)
1 gallon vanilla or chocolate ice cream,
  slightly softened
2 cups mini chocolate chips or sprinkles

1. Place and carefully flatten one scoop of ice cream on a cookie. Top with a second cookie and press down. Roll sides in chips or sprinkles. Place in a freezer bag and freeze immediately.

2. Allow sandwiches to freeze at least 2 hours before serving. Sandwiches will keep up to a week in freezer.

Makes twelve sandwiches.

BLACK-AND-WHITE MILKSHAKE

3 tablespoons chocolate syrup
1 cup milk
3 large scoops vanilla ice cream

1. Combine ingredients in a blender and blend on low until smooth and slightly foamy.

2. Serve immediately.

Serves two.

Variations: Try chocolate ice cream instead of vanilla for a chocolate shake, or use strawberry syrup and ice cream to make a strawberry shake, or substitute 1 tablespoon vanilla extract for the chocolate syrup to make a vanilla shake.

Ice Cream!

ICE-CREAM SODA

2 to 3 tablespoons chocolate or
    strawberry syrup
Chilled soda water
2 scoops ice cream
1 to 2 spoonfuls of whipped cream
    (optional)

1. Pour syrup into an 8-ounce soda glass and add soda water. Stir well until mixture is foaming at the top.
2. Add ice cream and top with whipped cream if desired.
3. Serve immediately with a straw and a long spoon.

Serves one.

Variation: substitute chilled root beer for the syrup and soda water mixture for a classic root-beer float.

WHIPPED CREAM

1/2 pint heavy cream
1 tablespoon vanilla extract
1 tablespoon white sugar

1. Combine ingredients in a large bowl and beat until stiff peaks form.
2. Serve immediately or cover and refrigerate for several hours until needed.

Makes two cups.

FOLLOW-THE-LEADER

An active and daring child should be chosen as leader. The others follow him or her, one behind the other, as closely as they can, doing as the leader does and going where the leader goes. The leader can choose to hop, skip, and jump; or crawl under and climb over obstacles. If anyone fails to accomplish any one feat, he or she leaves the line. The final person left in the line becomes the next leader.

Old-Fashioned Games

SIMON SAYS

One child is "Simon." The other children spread out near Simon and wait for his directions. Simon will give the group commands, like "touch toes," "rub belly," "hop on one foot," etc. If Simon precedes each command with the phrase "Simon says" the group has to follow his command. If his directions are not preceded with "Simon says," anyone who follows the command is out of the game. The last person in the game wins and is Simon in the next round. An adult can play this game with one child to test his or her concentration and focus.

TUG-OF-WAR

Find a strong, long rope and tie a piece of string at its center. Lay the rope down and and draw a corresponding line on the ground to show where the center is. The children divide into two groups and line up behind one another, holding on to opposite ends of the rope. On the signal "ready, set, go," both teams pull the rope as hard as they can. The children tug and tug until one team wins by forcing the other team to step over the line marked on the ground.

Growing Up

Time flies by so fast. With a little sunshine, water, and a lot of love, your grandchildren will sprout up before your eyes! The Body Collage is a fun and easy way to capture your grandchild's size and makeup at a particular age. When framed, it will make a great future gift to your grandchild, who will have long forgotten just how much his/her world revolved around Cheerios and dinosaurs! You and your grandchild will have great fun hunting for bits and pieces that reflect your grandchild's personality.

As you mark your grandchildren's height every year on your growth chart, you can marvel together at how much they've grown in the past year, look back at how cute and—hey! —short they were last year, and anticipate how much they will grow and change in the coming year.

BODY COLLAGE

Large paper bags or a large roll of kraft paper, markers, scissors, magazines, photographs, favorite things, glue

1. Cut open two large paper bags and tape them together so that you have a sheet that's a little longer and a little wider than your grandchild. Or you can use a section of a kraft paper roll.

2. Have your grandchild lie on the paper. Trace around their outline. This is a great opportunity to tickle!

3. Cut out the body shape.

4. Flick through magazines together to find pictures of things your grandchild likes. These could be anything from pictures of animals to computer games, cars, or musical groups. You also can add candy wrappers, pieces of cereal boxes, stickers, photographs—anything you can find to represent your grandchild's favorite things. Cut them out and paste them to the body shape.

5. Ask your grandchild to draw his/her face, shoes, etc., using the markers.

6. Make sure to add your grandchild's age so you can record for posterity his/her favorite things at this age. Let dry.

GROWTH CHART

A roll of paper about 7 feet by 4 inches (adding-machine paper works well), tape, measuring tape or ruler, permanent markers, colored pencils, thumbtacks

1. Unroll the paper and tape down top and bottom edges to the floor. Place measuring tape on top of paper, slightly off center. Using permanent marker and measuring tape, draw a straight line down middle of paper and mark off inches and feet. Remove measuring tape.

2. Write "Our Growing Family" on the top.

If you wish, let your grand-children decorate the chart with colored pencils. They can color every six inches with a different color. ("Grandma! I'm up to purple now!")

3. Tack the chart inside a closet door. Be sure the bottom of the chart touches the floor. (Alternatively, cut off the bottom 1 foot of the chart and position chart 1 foot above the floor.)

4. Using a different colored permanent marker, mark each grandchild's height and write the date. Holiday gatherings are the perfect time to update your chart every year

Grandmother Says...

One good turn deserves another.

>─┼─♦─○─♦─┼─<

Faith will move mountains.

>─┼─♦─○─♦─┼─<

Two wrongs do not make a right.

>─┼─♦─○─♦─┼─<

Honesty is the best policy.

>─┼─♦─○─♦─┼─<

Those who live in glass houses should not throw stones.

Love will find a way.

>─┼─♦─○─♦─┼─<

>─┼─♦─○─♦─┼─<

You can't please everyone.

The grass is always greener
on the other side.

It is no use crying over
spilt milk.

An ounce of prevention is
worth a pound of cure.

Life is just a bowl of cherries.

Laughter is the best medicine.

Look before you leap.

Classic Drinks

Grandma always needs to have a few refreshing and tummy-warming drinks up her sleeve. Start with favorites like lemonade and iced tea, and then impress them with a Shirley Temple, a sweet cocktail to make grandchildren feel grown up. On chilly days, warm up little ones with steamy cups of delicious hot chocolate or hot apple cider.

OLD-FASHIONED LEMONADE

1 cup water
2 cups white sugar
Juice of six lemons (1 1/2 cups)
8 cups cold water
1/4 cup sweetened cranberry juice
    (optional)
Ice cubes
2 lemons sliced thin and halved
3 or 4 sprigs fresh mint leaves

1. In a medium-size saucepan, combine 1 cup water and 2 cups sugar. Boil on low, stirring constantly, until sugar is completely dissolved, for about 5 minutes. Remove from heat.

2. When syrup has cooled (approximately 10 minutes), add lemon juice and stir well.

3. In a large pitcher, combine sugar and lemon syrup with 8 cups cold water. For pink lemonade, add the cranberry juice.

4. Serve lemonade over ice. Garnish with lemon slices and mint.

Serves six to eight.

SHIRLEY TEMPLE

Ice cubes
1 tablespoon maraschino cherry syrup
1 to 2 cups ginger ale
1 maraschino cherry

1. Fill an 8-ounce soda glass with ice, add syrup and ginger ale, and stir.

2. Garnish with cherry and serve immediately.

Serves one.

ICED SUN TEA

4 tea bags
8 cups cold water
2 lemons, sliced thin and halved
Ice cubes
Sugar

1. Combine water and tea bags in large pitcher. Place in a sunny spot and allow to sit for up to six hours.

2. Remove from sun, stir well, and remove tea bags. Serve over ice with lemon slices to garnish. Sweeten to taste.

Serves six.

MULLED APPLE CIDER

1 quart (8 cups) apple cider
Peel from 1/2 orange
1 1-inch peeled and sliced fresh ginger
1 teaspoon whole allspice
6 cinnamon sticks
Additional cinnamon sticks, one per cup
   (kids love to try to use them as straws!)

1. Put juice or cider in a large saucepan over the lowest heat.

2. Wrap up the remaining ingredients in a big piece of cheesecloth and put it into the pot, or put them in a strainer that hooks over the pot. Simmer at the lowest heat for 1 1/2 to 2 hours.

3. Throw away the spices, pour the cider into mugs, and add a cinnamon stick.

Serves six.

HOT CHOCOLATE

Whole milk (skim milk or water may be
   substituted)
Unsweetened cocoa
Sugar
Mini-marshmallows
Peppermint sticks
Whipped cream (*see page 35*)

1. Following portion directions on cocoa packaging, combine milk and cocoa in a medium-size saucepan on low heat.

2. Whisk the mixture as it heats until blended. Mixture should be warm but not boiling. Add sugar and continue to blend until hot.

3. Serve with marshmallows, whipped cream, and a peppermint stick.

Thumbelina

Once upon a time there was a young widow who wished to have a little child. She didn't know how she'd manage it, so she went to see a fairy. "Dear fairy, can you tell me where I might find a little child?"

"That's quite easy," replied the fairy. "Here is a rye seed. It is not an ordinary seed like those that grow in the farmers' fields. Take it home and plant it right away."

The widow thanked the fairy and gave her a gold coin. She raced home and planted the seed in a lovely flowerpot. To her amazement, the seed sprouted that very same day, and a beautiful red and gold tulip bud formed. The widow was delighted, and she leaned in to kiss the flower. The petals opened to reveal a tiny girl, no bigger than the widow's thumb. The widow called her Thumbelina.

The widow did her best to make a nice home for Thumbelina. She made her a little bed out of half a walnut shell and placed soft rose-petal blankets inside. A sugar bowl full of water served as

44

Thumbelina

her bathing pool, and one of the tulip petals served as a little boat. Thumbelina would amuse herself in the pool for much of the day. Then, at night, she would crawl between her rose-petal blankets and sing herself to sleep.

One night, a large toad came in through an open window. It jumped right up on the table where Thumbelina lay sleeping in her walnut-shell bed. "What a pretty creature," whispered the toad to herself. "She would make a fine wife for my son." So the toad took Thumbelina, bed and all, and hopped back to the muddy bank of the stream. Her son was even uglier than she was, and when he saw the pretty little girl, all he could say was Croak, croak, croak.

"Shush! Not so loud," said his mother. "You don't want to scare her off. Let's float her shell out to a lily pad in the stream. Meanwhile, we'll prepare a house for you two, here in the mud."

Thumbelina woke early the next morning to find herself stuck in the middle of the stream. She was very frightened and started to cry. Then the toads swam out to get her bed, to place it in the mud house they were building.

"Good morning, dear," said the mother toad. "This is my son, and you shall be his wife. We're building you a mud house, and we'll be back to

Thumbelina

get you when it is ready." Croak, croak, croak, was all her son could say, and they swam away with Thumbelina's bed, leaving her alone on the lily pad.

The fish in the stream heard the mother toad, and now they heard Thumbelina's sobs. They felt sad for the tiny girl, and so decided to help. They gathered under the lily pad and nibbled at the stem: Nibble, nibble, nibble. Finally, the pad broke free of the stem, and Thumbelina's raft floated down the stream.

Happy to be away from the toads, Thumbelina delighted in floating on the water. She watched the sun dance on the tiny waves, as a little breeze caressed her face.

Suddenly, a dragonfly swooped down and caught Thumbelina around the waist. He carried her up into a nearby tree. "You are a beautiful creature," he said. "I should like for you to be my wife." But when the other dragonflies came, they said that she was ugly. They laughed because she had only two legs and no wings. They did not trust her because she looked like the humans, who were the insects' worst enemies. Thumbelina's suitor started to believe what they said, so he carried her down to the ground and left her there.

Thumbelina was glad to be free again, able to enjoy the summer. She wove herself a tiny hammock out of blades of grass.

Thumbelina

She ate berries and nuts that she found. And every morning, she drank the dew that beaded on the leaves and grass.

She soaked up the warmth of summer, and even enjoyed playing in fall's long shadows. But once winter came, Thumbelina grew miserable. When the snowflakes fell, they were like huge ice blankets to a girl of her size. She was chilled to the bone, and knew that she had to find shelter. She traveled to a nearby field, where the remains of the wheat stalks stuck up out of the frozen ground. To her, the cut stalks were like tall trees.

As she walked, she came across a small opening in the ground. It was the entrance to a field mouse's hole. She called down to the mouse, and begged for a piece of grain.

"Come in, poor child," said Mouse. "Sit and eat with me." And when Mouse saw how sweet and lovely Thumbelina was, she invited her to stay for the winter. "You can help me clean the house and tell me stories." So Thumbelina stayed on, and they lived happily together in Mouse's cozy house.

"One of these days soon, we will have a visitor," said Mouse. "My neighbor, Mole, comes about once a week. He is wealthy and wise. He has a big house and wears a velvet coat. If you were to marry him, you would never want for anything. He is blind, and would take comfort in your storytelling."

Thumbelina

Well, Mole did pay a visit, in his black velvet coat. "Please sing for us, Thumbelina," said Mouse. So Thumbelina sang, and Mole fell in love with her lovely voice, but he was too shy to say so.

Mole had recently dug a new tunnel to Mouse's house, and he told Mouse that she and Thumbelina were welcome to use it. "Be warned, however," said Mole. "Someone has buried a dead bird in the tunnel. But don't be afraid of the good-for-nothing, dirty scavenger. He's quite frozen."

Mole's words about the bird upset Thumbelina. "Birds are not good for nothing," she thought to herself. "Their songs are the most beautiful in the world." That night, she could not sleep. She was thinking of the poor frozen bird. She got up and took a bit of hay and raw cotton into the tunnel. She carefully tucked them all around the bird, and said, "Farewell, beautiful swallow. Thank you for your summer songs." She laid her head down on his chest. Then she jumped! She heard a faint thump, thump coming from inside the swallow. She listened again, and it got stronger: THUMP! THUMP! Could it be? Was he still alive?!? Thumbelina was both excited and frightened, for the swallow was a very large creature. She quickly ran back to her bed and grabbed up her blankets to add to his cover.

Thumbelina

The next morning, she went to the tunnel again. The swallow was very weak, but he was alive. "Thank you, thank you, tiny girl," he said. "Soon I will be strong, and I can fly in the sunlight."

"But you can't," cried Thumbelina. "The snow is falling outside, and it is bitter cold. You have missed your chance to fly south, and must wait here until the spring comes. I will take care of you until then." She brought him water in a leaf cup, and little bits of grain that she saved from her dinner. Mole and Mouse never guessed it, but she nursed the swallow all winter long.

When spring arrived, Swallow said, "It is time for me to go. Will you come with me, Thumbelina? I can carry you on my back. We'll stay near the stream until fall, then we will fly south."

"Mouse has been so good to me," she replied. "I'm afraid that my leaving would make her very sad."

"Well, farewell, Thumbelina, and thank you," said the swallow. He darted out of the tunnel and up into the air, singing TWEET! TWEET!

One day, Mouse said, "Today we will start on your wedding dress. You'll marry Mole in the fall, you lucky thing." So Thumbelina and Mouse worked all summer long. Every chance she got, Thumbelina went outside to look for her friend the swallow. But she never saw him.

Thumbelina

Summer came to a close, and the wedding was only a few days off. Thumbelina went to the opening of the mouse's hole, and looked up to the sky. "Good-bye, bright earth," she said. "Goodbye green trees. Goodbye beautiful flowers. Goodbye fresh breezes. Goodbye golden sun!"

Then she heard a gentle song: TWEET! TWEET! She looked around and saw the swallow flying to her. She told him that she was supposed to marry the mole, but was unhappy. "Come with me, instead," said the swallow. "I'm flying south for the winter."

So she climbed on his back, and the swallow flew high into the sky. They traveled over lakes and streams, forests and fields, until they reached the warm country. The sun was as bright as Thumbelina had ever seen it, and it seemed higher, too. She smelled orange blossoms and saw green and red grapes, fat on their vines. Beautiful butterflies of many colors chased alongside of them. Finally, the swallow touched down on a hillside. There were many swallows' nests built into it. "This is my house," he said. Then he flew Thumbelina into the valley and set her down on a lovely pink flower. "This is your house."

Thumbelina was overwhelmed by the beautiful surroundings. Her flower was especially delightful. Suddenly, she saw something move. She looked closer and saw that it was a

Thumbelina

tiny man who also was sitting in the pink flower. He had beautiful brown hair and magical blue eyes. Thumbelina looked around and saw that all the flowers held similar creatures. This one was the king of them all because they all bowed to him.

"Oh, how handsome he is!" whispered Thumbelina.

The swallow had told the king how Thumbelina had saved his life and how sweet and gentle she was. "Would you like to be queen of the flowers?" the little king asked.

"Yes," said Thumbelina. The tiny creatures all greeted the new queen and cheered for the happy couple.

The swallow sang the best songs he knew.

"You shall not be called Thumbelina any more," said the tiny king. "Your new name is Maia."

"Farewell!" called the swallow when he flew back to the north, where he spent his summers. There he made his nest above the window of a storyteller. As he sang — TWEET! TWEET! — The storyteller wrote it all down, and that's how we know the tale of Thumbelina. ✦

Pecan Pie

How does one make pecan pies? Toasted, roasted, perhaps stir-fried? No, they actually come from Granny's oven—made with flour, patience, and lots of lovin'.

PASTRY

12 tablespoons (1 1/2 sticks) cold
   unsalted butter, cut into little pieces
3 cups all-purpose flour
3 tablespoons sugar
2 egg yolks, lightly beaten
About 1/4 cup ice water

FILLING

5 whole eggs
1 egg yolk
1 cup packed light brown sugar
2 tablespoons melted butter
2 teaspoons vanilla extract
2 to 3 tablespoons bourbon
3 cups pecan pieces, lightly toasted

1. In a mixing bowl, cut butter into the flour until it reaches the consistency of fine meal.

2. Sprinkle on the sugar and add lightly beaten egg yolks and ice water. Lightly blend together. Shape the dough firmly into a ball, wrap in waxed paper, and chill for at least 20 minutes.

3. Preheat oven to 350°F.

4. In a bowl, mix together all the filling ingredients except the pecans and blend well.

5. Roll out pastry on a lightly floured surface and fit it into a 9" pie pan. Place a layer of pecan pieces on the pastry. Pour filling mixture over the nuts. Bake for 1 hour, or until golden brown.

6. Cool to room temperature before serving.

Makes one 9-inch pie.

Balloons

This is the way
We blow our balloon.

Blow!

Blow!

Blow!

This is the way
We break our balloon.

Oh, oh, no!

Goosey, Goosey, Gander

Goosey, goosey, gander,

    Whither dost thou wander?

Upstairs and downstairs

    And in my lady's chamber.

The Farmer in the Dell

The farm-er in the dell, ____ the farm-er in the dell.

Heigh - ho the der - ry O! The farm-er in the dell. The

farm-er takes a wife, ____ the farm-er takes a wife.

Heigh - ho the der - ry O! The farm-er takes a wife. The

3. The wife takes the child,
The wife takes the child,
Heigh-ho, the derry O!
The wife takes the child.

4. The child takes the nurse...

5. The nurse takes the dog...

6. The dog takes the cat...

7. The cat takes the rat...

8. The rat takes the cheese...

9. The cheese stands alone,
The cheese stands alone,
Heigh-ho, the derry O!
The cheese stands alone.

Family Quilt

A handmade quilt can become a most treasured and beloved family heirloom. Sew simple shapes like stars, moons, and letters to the quilt squares to make a small crib quilt for your expected grandchild. Present your growing grandchild with a quilt made from favorite outgrown baby clothes, blankets, or crib bedding when they move to their first "grown-up" bed. Let older grandchildren each contribute special squares to be sewn together into a beautiful quilt that tells the story of your family.

Scissors, an iron, patterned and plain fabric pieces cut into $4^1/_2$" x $4^1/_2$" squares, straight pins, needle and thread, 66" x 96" twin flat sheet, thin quilt batting or flannel fabric, darning needle, wool yarn

1. Iron squares and arrange them on the floor in 24 rows of 18 squares each, creating a pleasing pattern.
2. To sew the first row, place the second square on top of the first, front sides facing each other. Pin along one side of the square and sew a $1/_4$-inch seam down this side. Remove pins.
3. Pin and sew the third square to the second square in the same manner. Continue until all eighteen squares are joined. Sew each of the 24 rows.
4. With front sides facing each other, pin and sew the first and second rows together along one edge. Repeat until all 24 rows are sewn together. Iron all seams flat.
5. Place your batting or flannel material on the backside of the quilt top and stitch it loosely to hold it together (these stitches may be removed later).
6. Smooth a bedsheet out on the floor and center your quilt on top of the sheet, front side down, batting facing up. Pin together.
7. Sew a $1/_4$-inch seam around your quilt, leaving a 6-inch opening in the middle of one side. Remove pins.
8. Turn your quilt right side out through the opening. Stitch opening closed.
9. Iron the quilt and lay it out on the floor. Hold the thickness of the quilt together using pins. Push the darning needle threaded with wool yarn through the middle of a quilt square, leaving about 5 inches of yarn on top. Push the needle back through the quilt from back to front and cut the yarn, leaving another 5 inches. Tie the pieces of yarn together in a square knot. Trim ends. Repeat in the middle of each square. Remove pins.

The Seven Ravens

Once upon a time there was a man who had seven sons. He loved his sons very much, but the man wished for a daughter. At last his wife had another child, and it was a girl! The father wanted to baptize his daughter at once, so he sent his sons down to the river to fetch water.

Well, the boys raced to help their father. In their haste to be the first to the river, they dropped their pitchers into the water. The boys splashed and scrambled after them, but the pitchers floated away. They didn't dare to go home empty-handed.

Meanwhile, their father waited for their return. What was taking so long? Impatiently he hollered, "I wish my naughty sons were all turned into ravens!" No sooner had the words left his mouth when he heard cawing and the sound of wings. Then he saw them: seven black birds flying up into the sky. "What have I done?" he cried.

Sorry as he was to see that his hasty wish had come true,

The Seven Ravens

the man did not know how to undo it. He and his wife tried to comfort themselves for their loss with their dear little daughter. They tried their best to keep the horrible truth from her, but as she grew up, she heard people talk about her seven brothers. The little girl wept. She was very sad to think that it was her birth that had caused her brothers' misfortune. She worried night and day. At last she decided that she would search the world for her brothers and set them free.

On her journey, she took her mother's ring and a loaf of bread. She walked on and on, until she came to the world's end. Then she came to the sun, but the sun looked much too hot and fiery; so she ran away quickly to the moon, but the moon was cold and chilly; so she ran until she came to the stars, and they were kind to her. The morning star rose up, gave her a little piece of wood, and said, "Use this to unlock the castle that stands on the glass mountain. There you will find your brothers." The little girl took the piece of wood and went on again, until she came to the door of the castle. She took out the little piece of wood, put it in the door, and opened it.

As she went in, a little dwarf came up to her and asked her what she wanted. "I am looking for my seven raven brothers."

The Seven Ravens

"They are my masters," said the dwarf, "but they are not at home. I am getting their dinner ready, so please come in and wait." The little dwarf disappeared into the kitchen and returned with seven little plates of food and seven little glasses of water, and set them upon the table. From each little plate, the little girl ate a small piece, and out of each little glass, she drank a small drop; but she let the ring that she had brought with her fall into the last glass.

Suddenly, she heard fluttering and cawing in the air, and the dwarf said, "Here come my masters." When they came in, they went straight for the table and looked for their little plates and glasses.

"Someone has been eating from my little plate," cawed the first brother.

"And someone has been drinking out of my little glass," said the second.

When the seventh came to the bottom of his glass, he found the ring and knew that it was his mother's. All the raven brothers looked at the ring and said, "Has our sister come to find us? Is she here to break the spell?"

When the little girl heard this, she came out from behind the kitchen door. The raven brothers turned back into themselves. They ran to hug their little sister, who had traveled so far and long to find them. Then, with hearts full of joy, they went home. ✦

I Know an Old Lady

Anonymous

I know an old lady who swallowed a fly.
I don't know why she swallowed a fly.
Perhaps she'll die.

I know an old lady who swallowed a spider.
It squirmed and wriggled and turned inside her.
She swallowed the spider to catch the fly.
I don't know why she swallowed a fly.
Perhaps she'll die.

I know an old lady who swallowed a bird.
How absurd! She swallowed a bird.
She swallowed the bird to catch the spider,
She swallowed the spider to catch the fly,
I don't know why she swallowed a fly.
Perhaps she'll die.

I know an old lady who swallowed a cat.
Think of that! She swallowed a cat.
She swallowed the cat to catch the bird,
She swallowed the bird to catch the spider,

She swallowed the spider to catch the fly.
I don't know why she swallowed a fly.
Perhaps she'll die.

I know an old lady who swallowed a dog.
She went the whole hog when she swallowed the dog.
She swallowed the dog to catch the cat,
She swallowed the cat to catch the bird,
She swallowed the bird to catch the spider,
She swallowed the spider to catch the fly,
I don't know why she swallowed a fly.
Perhaps she'll die.

I know an old lady who swallowed a cow.
I don't know how she swallowed the cow.
She swallowed the cow to catch the dog,
She swallowed the dog to catch the cat,
She swallowed the cat to catch the bird,
She swallowed the bird to catch the spider,
She swallowed the spider to catch the fly,
I don't know why she swallowed a fly.
Perhaps she'll die.

I know an old lady who swallowed a horse....
She's alive and well, of course!

Homemade Jams

Marty is my marvelous neighbor in San Francisco who went from no grandchildren to five in the space of three years. She is a marvelous cook and believes in starting the day with a delicious breakfast, complete with homemade jams.

RASPBERRY ——————

2 lbs. fresh raspberries (not too ripe)
4 cups (2 lbs.) white sugar

1. Place the raspberries in a saucepan and crush them slightly with a wooden spoon.

2. Cook over low heat until the fruit bubbles, stirring to keep it from sticking.

3. Add sugar slowly; keep stirring until it dissolves.

4. Increase heat, bringing the jam to a slow boil. Cook without stirring for 10 minutes, until jam sets.

5. Ladle into warmed, sterilized jars and seal while jam is hot.

Makes three cups.

STRAWBERRY ——————

2 lbs. fresh strawberries (not too ripe)
Juice from one orange
4 cups (2 lbs.) white sugar
1 teaspoon butter

1. Combine strawberries and orange juice in a saucepan over low heat. Bring to a boil and cover; simmer for 15 minutes.

2. Mash gently with a potato masher or a whisk.

3. Add sugar slowly; keep stirring until it dissolves.

4. Increase heat, bringing the jam to a slow boil. Cook without stirring for 10 minutes, until jam sets. Remove from heat and stir in butter.

5. Remove scum. Ladle into warmed, sterilized jars and seal while jam is hot.

Makes three cups.

Here is the Beehive

Here is the beehive.
Where are the bees?

Hidden away
Where nobody sees.

Watch and you'll see them
Come out of the hive—
One, two, three, four, five!

Bzzzz . . .
They're alive!

Every Branch of the Family

Discovering genealogy is a terrific family pastime. In these activities you can help your grandchildren, young and old, to understand where they fit in the family tree. It won't take much persuasion to get younger kids to dip their hands in plates of paint, and the naturally inquisitive older kids will jump at the opportunity to interview you and other family members. Work together to collect vital statistics, such as when and where each family member was born, lived, and passed away. Your grandchildren will learn that each family member is like a piece in a puzzle or a leaf on a tree.

FAMILY TREE

notebooks, pencils, large envelopes or plastic boxes (good for keeping the photographs, newspaper clippings, and documents you will collect)

1. The best place to start is with family members your grandchildren know best—themselves! Help the children to record their own full names, birthdays and birthplaces using their birth certificates. Then they can record their immediate family: father, mother, brothers, and sisters.

2. From here you will move backward, one generation at a time. The children can interview cousins, aunts, and uncles, and, of course, you! Encourage them to ask lots of questions and take lots of notes. They should record marriage dates, nicknames, occupations, interesting family stories, and, in the case of dead relatives, record when and where they died. Keep copies of all documentation.

3. Take the children on an excursion to your local courthouse. They have birth, marriage, and death certificates there, and may have the information you need.

4. Your local library may keep old newspapers on microfilm. You can look in the birth and obituaries sections. The obituaries will usually list the surviving family members. Ask if they have census records for the city too.

5. If the person you are looking for was born after 1930 you can contact the

Social Security office and request the records of that person. Their application forms will contain the date of birth, date of death, and who their parents were.

6. When you have finished compiling all of your historical data you can create a chart to illustrate your tree.

7. A family tree is a unique and special gift to a new grandchild. Add the name and date of birth of your newest grandchild—the newest blossom on your family tree. Frame and hang in your little darling's nursery.

HANDPRINT FAMILY TREE

Paint (in assorted colors), paintbrush, paper plates, white cotton fabric (an old sheet works well), permanent marker, fabric glue, 12-inch-long strong stick or wooden dowel, a long piece of string or ribbon

1. Paint a tree trunk with bare branches on the fabric.

2. Ask each of your grandchildren to pick out their favorite color from your selection of paints and spread a little of each color on paper plates.

3. Working from biggest to littlest hands, have each child dip his/her hands in their chosen paint and print them on the branches. Ask other family members—parents, aunts, uncles etc.—to get their "hands dirty" also to make your tree more complete.

4. Use permanent markers to write names next to handprints.

5. Children can paint birds, sky, sun, grass, and flowers etc. to complete the scene. Let dry.

6. Fold over a few inches at the top of the fabric and glue the edge to the back to form a sleeve for your stick or dowel. When the glue is dry, slide the stick or dowel through the sleeve.

7. Tie your ribbon or string to each end of the stick to make a hanger for your masterpiece. Ask your grandchildren to help you find the perfect place to display your family banner.

As I was going to St. Ives
I met a man with seven wives.
Every wife had seven sacks,
Every sack had seven cats,
Every cat had seven kits.
Kits, cats, sacks, and wives,
How many were going to St. Ives?

(one)

Going

A
stitch
in
time…

...saves nine.

Three Little Kittens

by Grace C. Floyd

Once upon a time there were three little Kittens, who loved to play and frisk about, and run after their own tails and each other's, and anything else that came in their way. One day their mother said, "Now children, I'm going to be very busy, so you can go out to play by yourselves, but be sure you are very good, and don't spoil your neckties nor lose your mittens." Then Mrs. Tabby washed their faces, tied their neckties afresh, put on their mittens, and sent them off. She watched them with pride till they were out of sight, then she bustled back into the kitchen and set to work to make a pie for dinner. "I'll give the children a treat," she thought, "they deserve it for they are the best children in the world and quite the prettiest, and how smart they look in their ties and mittens!" Meanwhile the Kittens were having fine games, and they rolled each other over until they were quite out of breath and sat down to rest. They were very warm too, so

Three Little Kittens

"The three little Kittens they took off their mittens,
When they had done their play,
But a Jackdaw so sly those six mittens did spy,
And stole them all away."

The Kittens did not notice the Jackdaw, and presently they jumped down off the wall and ran home, quite forgetting all about their mittens. They peeped in at the kitchen door, and there they saw, O, joy! their mother making a pie, a mouse pie too, which they loved more than anything. Then they scampered off again for they knew mother did not like to be disturbed when she was busy, so they had more games until they were called in to dinner. O, how quickly they clambered up on to their little stools, and took up their knives and forks ready to begin; the pie was baked such a lovely brown and it smelt so good! "Good children," said Mrs. Tabby, "now put your ties straight and smooth your mittens, but where are your mittens?" Then the Kittens looked down at their paws and saw that their mittens were gone, for

"The three little Kittens had lost their mittens,
So they began to cry
'O, Mammy dear, we greatly fear
That we have lost our mittens!'

Three Little Kittens

'Lost your mittens, you naughty Kittens,
Then you shall have no pie,'"

said their mother in an angry voice; "Miaou, Miaou, Miaou," cried all the poor little Kits, for they were very hungry, "Miaou, Miaou, Miaou," but Mrs. Tabby was very angry indeed, and she said, "No, you shall have no pie," and she carried it all lovely, brown and steaming, away. The three little Kittens cried bitterly for some time but at last said, "Well, it's no use crying, we must try to find our mittens." So they wrote in very large letters, on big sheets of paper, that three pairs of mittens were lost and that any person who found the same, should have a fine, fat mouse as reward. Then they pasted these bills up all over the place, and ran home to hunt for their mittens again. They searched for them everywhere; they peeped in the saucepan, though, as that had been on a high shelf all day with the lid on, they could hardly have got into there, and then they felt in the pockets of their little trousers, though they could hardly have been there either as they only wore them on Sundays, and this was Thursday. Afterwards they looked on the wall where they had been sitting and where they only now remembered that they had hung them, but no, they had gone and were nowhere to be found. But, at last, in the market, in the old Jackdaw's nest, they found them put out for sale, and Mr.

Three Little Kittens

Jackdaw close by as bold as brass, waiting for customers. Oh, how angry they were! They took old Jack, and they beat him and pulled out his feathers, and though he tried hard to peck, he was only one against three, so it was no use and at last he gave in and the Kittens took their mittens and ran home with them in high glee to their mother, calling out "O, Mammy dear, see here, see here, for we have found our mittens!" Mrs. Tabby was highly delighted too, and said, purring proudly and rubbing her paws,

> "Put on your mittens, you good little Kittens
> And you shall have some pie,
> Yes, you shall have some pie!"

So

> "The three little Kittens, they put on their mittens
> And soon ate up the pie."

Although it was a very big one, but then they were so hungry and it tasted so good. They felt very happy and comfortable afterwards until they happened to glance at their mittens, and then they saw that they had dropped some gravy on them.

> "O, Mammy dear, we greatly fear
> That we have soiled our mittens,"

Three Little Kittens

whimpered they, for they were honest little Kitties and always told mother directly they had done something naughty, and did not try to hide it.

"Soiled your mittens, you naughty Kittens!" said Mrs. Tabby, and she went and fetched her birch rod, to give them a whipping, so they all three ran off as fast as they could. But they were very sorry that they had made mother so angry, so they put their little heads together, and began to think what they could do to please her. "I know," said the eldest, "Let's wash our mittens." So they crept back to the house, very quietly, so that their mother should not hear, and they lighted the copper fire, and then they got a tub and some hot water, and soap and bluing, and they took off their mittens and put them in the tub, and then they rubbed and rubbed, and scrubbed and scrubbed, and boiled and rinsed them until they were quite clean. Mrs. Tabby saw, and she did not say anything, but she thought to herself, "I'm sure in all the world there were never such children, they are just as clever as they are pretty." When

"The three little Kittens had washed their mittens
They hung them out to dry,"

The Jackdaw was perched on a bough close by. He looked such a poor miserable old thing, not at all like the sleek Mr.

85

Three Little Kittens

Jackdaw he was when he stole the three little Kittens' mittens.
He said to himself "I could very easily steal those mittens again
if I wanted to, but no, never again will I do such a thing, for I'd
much rather have my own feathers than other people's mittens."
So the little Kittens left their mittens hanging on the line to dry,
and then ran indoors and said to their mother

> "O, Mammy dear, see here, see here,
> For we have washed our mittens."

Mrs. Tabby gave them each a kiss, saying,

> "Washed your mittens, you good little Kittens—
> But hark!—I hear a mouse close by,
> To catch him let us try."

So they all scampered after the mouse, and they caught him,
and a fine fat mouse he was too. ✦

Windy Days

*T*hese activities are all about energy! You can tap into your grandchildren's abundant energy to create and decorate a paper bag kite and wind chimes. Then harness Mother Nature's natural energy—WIND—to make them work!

PAPER-BAG KITES

Paper bags, markers, rubber bands, string

1. Help your grandchildren decorate paper bags using markers.

2. Blow air into the bags until they fully inflate like balloons and secure with rubber bands.

3. Attach a long piece of string or ribbon to each bag.

4. Find an open space for each grandchild to run with a paper-bag kite. Whose can fly the highest?

WIND CHIMES

Seashells, beads, bells, stones, string or nylon thread, glue, needle, plastic lid

1. Go on a treasure hunt and look for items that will create a lovely sound when they collide, such as seashells, bells, beads, and stones.

2. If the items are thin enough, like seashells, poke a hole through them with a nail. Then pull a piece of string or nylon thread through each hole and tie a knot. For heavier objects such as stones, wrap the string around the object a few times and rub nontoxic liquid glue over the string to hold it in place.

4. Find a colorful plastic lid to serve as the top of the wind chimes.

5. Poke holes through the top with a large sewing needle and pull the pieces of string or nylon thread though the holes; tie knots at the ends.

6. Finally, punch two holes in the center of the top and loop a piece of string through the holes, tying a knot on the inside. Hang your wind chime from a nail or the branch of a tree.

Polly Wolly Doodle

Oh, I went down South for to see my Sal, Sing

Pol - ly wol - ly doo - dle all the day. My ___

Sal, she is a spunk - y gal, Sing

Chorus

Pol - ly wol - ly doo - dle all the day. Fare thee

well, fare thee well, Fare thee

Polly Wolly Doodle

well my fair - y fay, For I'm

goin' to Lou' - si - an - a for to see my Su - sy - an - na, sing

Pol - ly wol - ly doo - dle all the day.

2. Oh, my Sal, she is a maiden fair,
Sing Polly wolly doodle all the day,
With curly eyes and laughing hair,
Sing Polly wolly doodle all the day.

Chorus

3. Behind the barn, down on my knees…
I thought I heard a chicken sneeze…

Chorus

4. He sneezed so hard with the whooping cough…
He sneezed his head and tail right off…

Chorus

5. Oh, a grasshopper sittin' on a railroad track…
A-pickin' his teeth with a carpet tack…

Chorus

6. Oh, I went to bed but it wasn't any use…
My feet stuck out like a chicken roost…

Chorus

An Elegant Tea Party

Gather your family together for a delicious tea party. Brew a bracing pot of tea or make iced tea or lemonade *(page 43)*. These wonderful scones are an old family recipe from Great-grandma Coughlan. To complete your menu, add fresh fruit, little cucumber and butter sandwiches (thinly slice peeled cucumber and bread, and remove crust from bread), lemon squares *(page 180)*, cookies *(page 198)*, and jams *(page 71)*. For an extra special tea, why not make strawberry shortcake *(page 130)!* With a cup of tea in hand and good things to eat, you can relax, chat, enjoy your family, and savor a lovely afternoon.

NANA'S SCONES

1 1/2 cups all-purpose flour
1/2 cup whole wheat flour
1/3 cup granulated sugar
1 tablespoon baking powder
6 tablespoons chilled, unsalted butter
1/3 cup baking raisins
1/2 cup heavy whipping cream
2 large eggs, beaten

1. Preheat oven to 375°F.
2. In a large bowl, combine all-purpose and wheat flour, sugar, and baking powder.
3. Using a pastry blender or two knives scissor fashion, cut in the butter until the mixture resembles coarse crumbs. Stir in the raisins, mixing well.
4. Combine heavy cream, reserving 1 tablespoon, and 1 beaten egg in a small bowl. Add to flour mixture. Stir until just moistened. Do not overmix.
5. Transfer the dough to a lightly floured surface and knead gently. Roll or pat the dough into a circle about 7 inches across and 1 1/2 inches thick.
6. Lightly flour the rim of a glass and press into dough, making perfect rounds. Repeat until all dough is used. Place the scones on an ungreased cookie sheet.
7. Whisk egg and 1 tablespoon heavy cream. Brush egg mixture over scones.
8. Bake for approximately 15 to 20 minutes, or until lightly browned.
9. These are especially delicious when served warm with butter and preserves.

Makes six scones.

Here is the Church

Here is the church.

Here is the steeple.

Open the doors.

And see all the people.

My Turtle

This is my turtle.
He lives in a shell.
He likes his home very well.

He pokes his head out
When he wants to eat.

And he pulls it back
When he wants to sleep.

MULBERRY BUSH

The children form into a ring, and holding hands run around singing:

> Here we go round the mulberry bush,
> > the mulberry bush, the mulberry bush;
> Here we go round the mulberry bush on a cold
> > and frosty morning.

Then, unloosening hands, they pretend to wash them, singing:

> This is the way we wash our hands,
> > wash our hands, wash our hands;
> This is the way we wash our hands on a cold
> > and frosty morning.

They then go around in a ring again, adding verses to wash faces, put on clothes, go to school, and anything they like.

RING AROUND THE ROSEY

At least two players join hands, forming a ring, and walk around singing:

> Ring around the rosey
> A pocket full of posies
> Ashes, ashes,
> We all fall down.

After singing the last line, players collapse to the floor. Then they get up and begin singing all over again.

Embroidery

*E*mbroidery can transform the plainest baby clothes into covetable family heirlooms. Your grandchildren will love seeing their names stitched onto clothes and on fabric-covered frames and books. Almost anything can be given Grandma's loving touch with embroidery, including towels, pillows, Christmas stockings and even stuffed dolls. When framed, the embroidered words of your grandchild's favorite rhyme or song make a special and thoughtful gift.

MAKE IT PERSONAL

Disappearing-ink pen, item to embroider, hoop (optional), needle, thread or fine yarn, scissors

1. Carefully trace your grandchild's name in block letters onto your fabric using the disappearing-ink pen. Cotton and linen are good fabric choices if the item is intended for wear.

2. Using a hoop is optional but recommended, as it can help keep your stitches even and prevent puckering in your fabric.

3. Following the instructions below, fill in the outline of each letter of your grandchild's name with the satin stitch. You can stitch each letter in a different color thread or different hues of the same color family to make the design a little more interesting.

4. After you have completed all of the stitches, remove the fabric from the hoop. Lay the embroidered piece face down on a thick terry towel. Carefully press with a warm iron.

5. The finished piece may be framed.

SATIN STITCH

Made at an angle, these parallel stitches fill in the outline of a design that incorporates shape or width. Insert needle from wrong to right side of fabric, coming out at point A. Insert needle at B; pull it back through at C, right next to A. Keep stitches tight and flat to ensure a smooth finish.

Grandmother Says...

The best things in life are free.

Beauty is only skin deep.

All that glitters is not gold.

Don't put all your
eggs in one basket.

Never judge by appearances.

>─┼─◆─○─◆─┼─<

Money does not grow on trees.

>─┼─◆─○─◆─┼─<

Things are not always
what they seem.

>─┼─◆─○─◆─┼─<

You can't tell a book
by its cover.

>─┼─◆─○─◆─┼─<

Don't go near the water until
you learn how to swim.

>─┼─◆─○─◆─┼─<

Waste not, want not.

>─┼─◆─○─◆─┼─<

A penny saved is a penny earned.

Stone Soup

Once upon a time there was a great famine, which swept the land. Villagers desperately guarded their food, hiding it away from their friends and neighbors. One day, a peddler came through the village looking to trade his goods for something to eat. But the villagers quickly informed him that there was not a bite of food to be found for miles.

"Well," he said, "that's no problem. I'll just make some stone soup to share with all of you." Out of his wagon he pulled a large iron kettle and filled it with water he had gotten from a stream a few hours back. Next he pulled three smooth stones out of a velvet bag, and dropped them into the water.

Soon, more people gathered to see what was happening. "I'm making stone soup," announced the peddler. "Stick around and have some."

"Stone soup? Hmmm... I have some cabbage in my cellar," offered one villager. "Would it taste good with the stones?"

Stone Soup

"Of course," said the peddler. "There's nothing better than stone and cabbage soup." So the villager went off to fetch the cabbage.

"Well, I think I have a little cured ham," offered the butcher. "Would that help the flavor?"

"You bet it would," said the peddler. "Bring it on out." So the butcher went off to fetch the ham.

"I may have a few potatoes," offered another villager. "Would you like them for the soup?"

"That would be just great!" said the peddler. "Potatoes are the perfect addition."

So it went, with the villagers offering all sorts of ingredients, such as carrots, onions, beans, herbs, and so on, until a delicious meal was ready for all to enjoy. After everyone had had their fill of the wonderful soup, the villagers asked the peddler if he might sell his magical stones. He replied, "I am sorry, but there is no amount of money that could persuade me to part with my stones." So the villagers had to content themselves with what he had given them. They thanked the peddler and sent him on his way. But from that time on, well after the famine was over, they talked about the finest soup they had ever tasted. ✦

Swing, Swing

by William Allingham

Swing, swing,
Sing, sing,
Here! my throne and I am a king!
Swing, swing,
Sing, sing,
Farewell, earth, for I'm on the wing!

Low, high,
Here I fly,
Like a bird through sunny sky;
Free, free,
Over the lea,
Over the mountain, over the sea!

Soon, soon,
Afternoon,
Over the sunset, over the moon;
Far, far,
Over all bar,
Sweeping on from star to star!

No, no,
Low, low,
Sweeping daisies with my toe.
Slow, slow,
To and fro,
Slow—slow—slow—slow.

Pot Roast

My friend Lenore's mother served this to me recently at a dinner party. She is a great-grandmother and this is one of her most requested recipes. Serve with small steamed red potatoes, fettucini, or mashed potatoes. It will satisfy your entire family.

2 to 3 tablespoons vegetable oil
2 large yellow onions, diced
2 to 3 crushed garlic cloves (optional)
2 1/2 to 3 lbs. lean beef brisket
Salt & pepper (to taste)
1 cup boiling water
1 large can plum tomatoes, crushed
6 medium-size potatoes, peeled and quartered
4 to 6 large carrots, peeled and quartered
Several handfuls fresh green peas or
    1 package frozen (optional)

1. Heat oil in a Dutch oven or large stockpot.
2. Add diced onion and brown lightly. Add garlic and sauté for 1 to 2 minutes.
3. Add meat and brown on all sides over high heat, around 6 to 7 minutes.
4. Add salt and pepper. Reduce heat and add boiling water. Cover pot tightly.
5. Simmer on low heat for 45 minutes.
6. Add crushed tomatoes, cover again, and simmer while preparing vegetables.
7. Stir vegetables into pot.
8. After meat has cooked a total of 2 hours, remove it carefully and lay it on a board. Slice thinly.
9. Return meat to pot and simmer 1 hour, until everything is soft and tender.
10. During the last 1/2 hour you may add fresh or defrosted peas.

Serves four to six.

Sour-Cream Spinach Casserole

Kelly is not yet a grandmother, but her eight-year-old daughter Saxon told me this is her mom's best recipe, so I have got to believe that when Saxon has children it will be at the top of her list. Kelly believes in cooking with organic ingredients, and serves this every Thanksgiving with her turkey.

1 10-oz. bag frozen chopped spinach
1/2 bag garden herb croutons (about 2 1/2 cups)
1 1/4 cups sour cream
1 packet onion soup mix
1 1/4 tablespoons melted butter

1. Put frozen spinach in a fine strainer over a bowl to drain and defrost. After 2 to 3 hours, when spinach is defrosted, press out the excess liquid with a spoon.
2. Preheat oven to 350°F.
3. Crush croutons in a plastic bag with a rolling pin or skillet until they are closer to the consistency of bread crumbs.
4. Mix spinach, sour cream, and onion soup mix in a large bowl.
5. Transfer to a small casserole dish and spread out evenly.
6. Flatten the top and pour the crushed croutons evenly over the surface.
7. Drizzle butter with a spoon evenly over the croutons.
8. Cover with a lid (or aluminum foil) and bake for 1/2 hour, until croutons are a light golden brown.

Serves four as a side dish.

We can do no great things—
only small things with
great love.

—Mother Teresa

Homemade Paper

Making beautiful paper is much easier than you think. Try this once and you may find yourself experimenting frequently with different scraps and notions. Use your creations for stationery, cards, picture frames, and book covers (page 128). Let your grandchildren help gather, rip, mix, mash, and roll!

Scrap paper (see Step 1); old window screen; wire cutters; 4 pieces of wood to frame screen; nails and hammer or heavy-duty stapler; blender; water; small flowers, leaves, feathers, or decorative threads; plastic tub large enough to accommodate screen; glue or cornstarch; two large pieces of felt; rolling pin; newspaper; laundry line or twine; clothespins

1. You will need approximately one cup of loosely packed scraps per 8- by 11-inch sheet of paper. Many different colors can be mixed, but it is best to keep the colors light in hue, with little or no printed ink on them, if you plan to use the paper for writing. Choose paper with both long fibers (thicker and harder-to-rip paper, like construction paper) and short fibers.

2. Rip your scrap paper into pieces about 1 inch square. Soak short- and long-fiber paper in separate bowls of water for 15 minutes.

3. Cut your window screen to slightly larger than the paper size you want. Place the screen on top of your four pieces of wood and nail or staple it in place. (Or buy a small, adjustable window screen at a hardware store.)

4. Fill a blender about 3/4 full with clean water. Take a handful of the shorter fiber scraps and put them into the blender. Cover the top and blend on medium-high for a few seconds. The mixture, called pulp, will start to look like runny oatmeal.

5. Add various scraps, short fibers first, one by one, and give a short blast with the blender each time. Don't fill the blender more than 3/4 full.

6. Add decorative items, like threads and flowers, to the mixture, but do not blend.

7. Fill a large tub with clean water. Pour the pulp into the tub and swirl it around. The pulp should be distributed evenly throughout the water before you start dipping.

8. Add a few drops of glue or a tablespoon of cornstarch to the tub and mix it in thoroughly.

9. Hold your screen with the frame on top and dip it in the tub at an angle until it's fully immersed. Move screen back and forth, collecting the pulp on top of it. Lift the screen slowly out of the tub, keeping it flat to catch as much pulp as possible.

10. You should have collected enough pulp on the screen to make one sheet of paper—the pulp should fill the screen evenly to the inner edges of the frame. Allow the water from the pulp to drip off the screen. Hold the frame above the tub until only a few drops of water remain on the screen.

11. Lay a sheet of felt down on a flat table-top. Turn your frame over on top of the felt. The pulp should drop out easily. If not, you can gently tap the frame on the felt.

12. Lay another felt on top of the pulp. Take a rolling pin and press down on the pile to squeeze out the excess water. Start at one end and roll firmly and evenly across the pile a few times to get as much water out as possible. The rolling action presses the fibers together.

13. Carefully remove the top layer of felt from the pulp.

14. Carefully take up two corners of your paper by rolling them back with your fingers. Hold a corner with each hand and gently peel the sheet off the bottom felt. Use newspaper to absorb any excess moisture from paper.

15. Clip your fresh sheet of paper to the laundry line or twine with clothespins. Leave to dry for a few hours. Avoid damp areas, as mold might grow on the paper.

There was an old woman
tossed in a basket,
　　Seventeen times as high as the moon;
But where she was going
no mortal could tell,
　　For under her arm she carried a broom.

"Old woman, old woman, old woman," said I,
　　"Whither, oh whither, oh whither so high?"
"To sweep the cobwebs from the sky;
　　And I'll be with you by-and-by."

Old Woman

The Mountain and the Squirrel

by Ralph Waldo Emerson

The mountain and the squirrel
Had a quarrel;
And the former called the latter "Little Prig."
Bun replied,
"You are doubtless very big;
But all sorts of things and weather
Must be taken in together,
To make up a year
And a sphere.
And I think it no disgrace
To occupy my place.
If I'm not so large as you,
You are not so small as I,
And not half so spry,
I'll not deny you make
A very pretty squirrel track;
Talents differ; all is well and wisely put;
If I cannot carry forests on my back,
Neither can you crack a nut."

The Little Mermaid

Once upon a time, there was a little mermaid who lived far out to sea, where the water is the darkest blue and so deep that no anchor can touch the bottom. She wasn't just any girl with a fish tail; she was the daughter of the sea king, and the granddaughter of the noble queen mother. Nevertheless this mermaid, who had so much to be thankful for—good friends, loving sisters, a wonderful father, a doting grandmother, and all the treasures you could imagine—was really quite miserable.

Ever since her grandmother had first told her stories about the great ships upon the surface of the sea, she had longed to know more about the lives of the humans: What did they look like? Were they like her? What did they do for adventure? Her grandmother, too, had been very curious about the "upper world" in her youth. She tried her best

The Little Mermaid

to paint a full picture of human life for her youngest granddaughter. But the little mermaid's father thought the surface was a dangerous place, and made her promise not to go there until after her fifteenth birthday.

Well, one day she quite forgot her promise, and swam up to the sunlight. She came up close to a sailing ship. Careful not to be noticed, she spied on the people aboard. Among the passengers was a handsome prince. The little mermaid fell in love with him at first sight.

Suddenly a storm broke out, and the ship was violently tossed on the waves. The crew was forced to jump overboard, and the prince struggled to stay afloat. Without hesitation, the little mermaid swam to him and pulled him to the nearest shore, next to his castle. Wanting to make sure he was all right, she waited in the surf, out of sight. When he awoke, he saw a beautiful woman standing over him. Thinking she was the one who saved him, he smiled at her. Well, it turns out she was a princess, and the prince asked her to be his wife. They were to be married in a week.

The Little Mermaid

The little mermaid was heartbroken. She swam down to her father's kingdom as fast as she could. But since she was not allowed to go to the surface, she dared not tell anyone in her family about what had happened—not even her beloved grandmother. The next day, she visited the dreadful sea witch and asked for her help. "I know what you have come for, my pretty," said the witch. "If you agree to leave your tongue behind, then I will grant your wish." The little mermaid agreed. "Well," snorted the witch, "you can't expect to win the prince's heart wearing those fins." Legs magically appeared where the little mermaid's tail had been. "I will give you three days to make him fall in love with you. If you should fail, I will melt you into foam," the sea witch cackled. "Your soul will be lost forever!" The little mermaid sped up to the surface, for she could no longer breathe as a fish.

She swam back to the shore where she had left the prince. He was walking on the beach with his dog when he spotted her. She seemed familiar to him, but he could not remember where they

The Little Mermaid

had met. And the little mermaid couldn't tell him that it was she who saved him from the shipwreck because she no longer had her voice. So they just smiled at each other, and he invited her to stay at his castle. As the days passed, he grew very fond of the little mermaid, but he was already engaged to the woman he thought had saved him.

When the week was through, the prince married the princess, and the little mermaid returned to the shore and waited to be turned to foam. Instead, she saw her sisters in the surf. They had all lost their hair. They had sold it to the sea witch in exchange for the little mermaid's life. Her oldest sister gave her a tiny dagger and told her she must stab the prince through the heart while he slept. Then she would regain her tail and become a mermaid again.

That night, the little mermaid went to the wedding ship where the prince and princess slept. She bent over their bed, and gave them each a tender kiss. She glanced down at the gruesome

The Little Mermaid

dagger she held, and threw it into the sea. Then she jumped overboard, and immediately turned to foam. It appeared that the sea witch's curse had come to pass after all, and that the little mermaid's soul was lost forever.

But a wonderful thing happened. The sun's rays warmed the foam and lifted it up to the sky. The little mermaid's loving nature and the unselfishness of her deed caused her to float into paradise. She became one of the spirits of the air who watch over all the little children of the world. If you look very carefully, you just might see her sitting on a cloud or sliding down a rainbow. ✦

MARBLES

Young children (but not so young that marbles would be a choking hazard) can play a simplified version of Ring Taw, the most popular marble game during settler times. Draw a ring on the ground and place several marbles inside. Children practice shooting a marble from outside the ring, trying to knock other marbles out of the ring. Older children can play against each other "for keeps," keeping marbles they knock out. The one with the most marbles wins.

Old-Fashioned Games

TIDDLYWINKS

Give each child a quarter and a dime. Place dimes around a bowl about a foot away. Take turns flipping the dimes or "winks" into the bowl with the quarter. To flip, hold the quarter between thumb and forefinger and press down on the edge of the dime. The first child to pot his or her wink wins. A young child can play by practicing flipping a dime onto a plate.

THE FEATHER GAME

The players stand close together in a bunch. One of them takes a feather and blows it up into the air. The other players must keep it afloat by their breath. If anyone allows it to sink to the ground he or she must pay a forfeit. Two players can take turns to see who can keep the feather in the air the longest.

Grandmother Says...

Practice makes perfect.

Live and learn.

Opportunity seldom knocks twice.

As you make your bed,
so must you lie in it.

Actions speak louder than words.

Experience is the best teacher.

Make hay while the sun shines.

*Always put your best
foot forward.*

*Where there's a will
there's a way.*

As you sow, so shall you reap.

The first step is the hardest.

Never too old to learn.

*Nothing ventured,
nothing gained.*

You win some,
you lose some.

Bound with Love

Sometimes you can judge a book by its cover. Homemade books bound with love and imagination hint at the importance of what hides inside. Be creative with the book cover, paper, decorative additions, and contents, and you will have a book for any occasion.

HANDMADE BOOK

Paper glue or paste, two 8"x 8" pieces of cardboard, homemade paper or gift wrap, scissors, hole punch, 8"x 2" piece of cardboard, pencil, 8" x 8" sheets of paper, ribbon

1. Carefully paste handmade paper to the front and back of your cardboard covers. Let dry.
2. Mark four spots for holes along the 8" x 2" piece of cardboard. The first hole will be 1 inch from the top and 1/2 inch in from the edge. Punch the other three holes each 2 inches apart in a straight line below. This will be your hole-punching guide.
3. Use the guide and pencil to mark holes on covers and interior pages. Punch. Stack the covers and pages so the holes align.
4. Cut ribbon into four 6-inch pieces. Thread ribbons through the holes of your book and tie into bows, leaving a little slack so the pages turn easily.

BOOK IDEAS

- Use heavier text stock to make a family photo album.
- Bind together all your secret recipes to make a lasting heirloom.
- Decoupage *(see page 136)* the covers with old Christmas card cutouts to make a family Christmas book.
- Use felt or other fabric to make a soft book for your youngest grandchildren. Sew on felt or fabric shapes.
- Make a "touch and tickle book" using cardboard for the interior. Make cutouts in the cardboard pages and glue interesting textures to the back of each page: feathers, cotton balls, sandpaper, silk.
- Glue foam-core board to the cardboard covers and then cover with a pretty fabric. Bind with narrow strips of the same fabric.
- Bind together a whole book of homemade paper *(see page 110)* to make a beautiful journal.

Strawberry Shortcake

"Strawberry shortcake cream on top, tell me the name of your sweetheart." Grandmother is surely a sweetheart when she serves this classic favorite. Make the cakes ahead of time and let your grandchildren help assemble this pretty confection when they arrive.

3 cups sugar
16 tablespoons (2 sticks) butter,
    room temperature
6 eggs
8 ounces sour cream
2 tablespoons vanilla
4 cups flour
1/2 teaspoon baking soda
3 cups fresh whipped cream *(see page 32)*
2 pints fresh strawberries

1. Preheat oven to 350°F. Butter and flour two 8- or 9-inch layer pans. Set aside.

2. In a large bowl, cream together sugar and butter. Beat in eggs one at a time, then add sour cream and vanilla and mix well.

3. In a separate bowl, combine flour and baking soda, then add gradually to egg mixture.

4. Pour into prepared pans. Bake for 1 hour to an hour and 15 minutes. Let cool 30 minutes before turning cakes out of pans. Set aside and allow to cool completely.

5. While cakes are cooling, prepare whipped cream and refrigerate.

6. Rinse, clean, and halve strawberries. Set aside on paper towel.

7. Once cakes are cool, begin assembly. Slice each cake in half crosswise so that your shortcake has a total of four layers. Spread whipped cream over one layer, top with strawberries and the next layer of cake and repeat to build your cake.

Note: Cakes may be prepared up to 24 hours ahead of time. Strawberries and whipped cream may be prepared several hours ahead of time. But cake should not be assembled until less than an hour before serving, to prevent sogginess.

Makes one 8- or 9-inch cake.

Chocolate Layer Cake

This dense, yummy cake, spread with rich chocolate icing, is perfect for birthday celebrations. One bite and everyone will know this is something Grandmother made from scratch with a lot of love. Your grandchildren will melt with delight.

CAKE

2 1/4 cups white flour, sifted
1 1/2 cups white sugar
3 teaspoons baking powder
1 teaspoon salt
8 tablespoons (1 stick) butter,
    room temperature
2/3 cup milk
1 tablespoon vanilla
1/3 cup milk
2 eggs

CHOCOLATE ICING

1 stick (8 tablespoons butter)
4 squares unsweetened bakers' chocolate
1 box confectioners' sugar
1 tablespoon vanilla
1/3 cup milk

1. Heat oven to 350°F. Butter and flour two 8- or 9-inch layer pans. Set aside.

2. In a large bowl, mix together flour, sugar, baking powder, and salt.

3. Continue to mix, slowly adding butter, 2/3 cup milk, and vanilla. Beat vigorously.

4. Add another 1/3 cup milk and eggs. Beat for 2 minutes, then pour into baking pans. Bake 30 to 35 minutes. Let cool before turning out of pans.

5. To make the icing, melt butter and chocolate together in small saucepan.

6. Pour mixture into large bowl, add remaining ingredients and beat until smooth.

7. When cakes are completely cool, ice cake with chocolate.

Makes one 8- or 9-inch cake.

FOX AND HEN

One of the players is chosen to be the fox and another to be the hen. All the others are chicks. They form a line behind the hen, one behind another, each holding on to the waist of the child in front. The hen spreads her arms wide to protect her chicks while the fox, in front of her, tries to run past her arms to grab a chick from the line. The game is over when all the chicks are captured.

FREEZE TAG

Children scatter in an open area before one player, who is "It," chases after them. Whoever "It" tags must freeze like ice on the spot until an unfrozen player is able to tag and unfreeze them. The child who is "It" must tag and freeze all the children, chasing new ones down as well as guarding already frozen victims. To make the game easier, players can remain frozen, and not be "melted" or saved.

HIDE-AND-SEEK

One child dubbed "It" hides his or her eyes at a spot called "home" and counts to twenty. The other children run away and hide. The child who is "It" calls out "Ready or not, here I come!" and begins searching for the other players. He or she must catch a player before they scramble to safety at "home." The one caught is "It" next time. If none are caught, then the child who is "It" remains so for another round.

Little Nanny Etticoat

Little Nanny Etticoat
In a white petticoat,

And a red nose;

The longer she stands
The shorter she grows.

(a candle)

Picture Perfect: Frames

Is there any better way to display all of those pictures of your grandchildren than in frames they helped you create? Decoupage is the art of decorating with paper cutouts. It is a simple technique and can be used to decorate everything from shoeboxes to furniture.

Next time you take your grandchildren to the beach, bring a little beach home with you to decorate a frame. (Don't forget to take photographs of your day of fun in the sun with the children.)

DECOUPAGE FRAME

old magazines and greeting cards, scissors, water, plastic bowl, Elmer's glue, paintbrush, plain wood picture frame

1. Go through used magazines and old greeting cards with your grandchildren to find and cut out pictures you like.

2. Pour a small amount of water into a plastic bowl and slowly add glue, stirring constantly until the mixture is a soupy consistency.

3. Use a paintbrush to spread some of the mixture onto a small area of the frame. Apply cutouts to this area, over-lapping to cover completely.

4. Add more glue mixture to another area of the frame and continue in this fashion until the entire wood area of the frame is covered. Apply a thin coat of glue mixture to the entire area to seal the pictures in permanently and create a clear glaze when dry. Leave to dry.

SEASHELL FRAME

Water, plastic bowl, glue, paintbrush, plain lucite or glass frame, sand, seashells

1. Mix glue with water as for decoupage frame. Spread mixture all around the edge of frame—don't worry about making it even.

2. Lay frame faceup and sprinkle sand on top of the glue. Shake off excess sand and then glue seashells along the bottom edge of frame. Leave to dry.

3. Insert a photograph from your day at the beach with your grandchildren.

Picture Perfect: Games

Kids love to look at themselves. With these activities your grandchildren will be so busy looking for matching pictures of themselves and trying to reassemble the puzzle that they won't realize they are enhancing their concentration skills and beefing up their memory muscles! Good going, Grandma!

MEMORY GAME

Camera with film, scissors

1. Photograph your grandchildren, their favorite toys, and other family members (don't forget the family pet). Have two sets of prints made.

2. Cut all the pictures to uniform size, trimming matching pictures in the same way. Round off corners.

3. Shuffle the "deck" and then spread the photos facedown on a tabletop.

4. Have each child turn up one card and then another, in search of a matching pair, turning up two cards at a time. If they have different pictures, they're flipped facedown again. If a match, the photos are removed from the board. The game continues until all matching pairs have been found.

PICTURE PUZZLE

Camera with film, glue, posterboard, scissors

1. Take a photo of your grandchild or grandchildren together and have it developed as a 5- by 7-inch (or larger) photograph.

2. Enlist the little ones to help you glue the photo to a posterboard.

3. After the glue is dry, cut the picture into lots of fun shapes. Mix up the pieces on top of the table.

4. Hey presto! You have a picture puzzle. For a little added fun, write a little note, like "Grandma loves you," on the back of the photograph before you cut it up. The kids can flip the pieces over and assemble the word puzzle to find the hidden message!

The Gingerbread Man

by Rowena Bennett

The gingerbread man gave a gingery shout:
"Quick! Open the oven and let me out!"
He stood up straight in his baking pan.
He jumped to the floor and away he ran.
"Catch me," he called, "if you can, can, can."

The gingerbread man met a cock and a pig
And a dog that was brown and twice as big
As himself. But he called to them all as he ran,
"You can't catch a runaway gingerbread man."

The gingerbread man met a reaper and a sower.
The gingerbread man met a thresher and mower;
But no matter how fast they scampered and ran
They couldn't catch up with a gingerbread man.

Then he came to a fox and he turned to face him.
He dared Old Reynard to follow and chase him;
But when he stepped under the fox's nose
Something happened. What do you s'pose?
The fox gave a snap. The fox gave a yawn,
And the gingerbread man was gone, gone, GONE.

Rapunzel

Once upon a time there was a couple who dreamed of having a child. Finally, their prayers were answered and they happily awaited the birth of their baby. Now, this couple lived in a house that overlooked the loveliest garden, which was surrounded by a high wall. No one dared to enter this garden, for it belonged to an evil sorceress.

One day, the woman looked down into the garden and saw a bed full of the finest rapunzel lettuce. The leaves looked so fresh and green that she longed to eat them. Day by day, as she waited for her child to be born, her craving grew until she couldn't stand it. "If I don't get some of that rapunzel, I will certainly die," she moaned to her husband.

Her husband loved her dearly and was determined to help her. At dusk, he climbed over the wall and dropped into the sorceress's garden. He quickly gathered some rapunzel and returned to his wife. It tasted so good that she desperately wanted more.

Rapunzel

So at dusk the next day, her husband set off to fetch her more rapunzel. Over the wall he went, but when he reached the other side he drew back in fear. Standing before him was the evil sorceress herself. "How dare you climb into my garden and steal my lettuce?" she said, with an angry stare. "You will pay for this!"

"Oh!" he pleaded, "I beg your pardon, but I had to come. My wife saw your rapunzel from our window, and thought that she'd rather die than not have some. I came to get it to save both she and our unborn child."

The sorceress's anger quickly faded, and a smile crept across her face. "If what you say is true, then you may take as much rapunzel as you wish, on one condition: Your newborn shall be mine!"

The man had no choice but to agree, and as soon as the child was born the sorceress appeared to claim her. She named her Rapunzel, and took her away.

When the girl reached the age of twelve, the sorceress locked her in a tower in the middle of the forest. The tower had no stairs or doors, but only a small window near the very top. When the sorceress wished to get in, she stood down below and called out,

Rapunzel

Rapunzel, Rapunzel,
Let down your hair.

Rapunzel would unpin her long, golden braids and let them fall down from the window. The sorceress used the braids to climb the sixty-foot wall of the tower. She always left before dark, and lonely Rapunzel would sing herself to sleep.

One evening, a prince was riding through the forest and happened to pass by the tower. Upon hearing Rapunzel's sweet song, he stopped and listened. The prince longed to see the woman whose voice was so delightful, but he could not find the tower door. He returned to the tower every day to listen to the enchanting song. One day, the prince arrived earlier than usual and did not hear any singing; so he stretched out under the shade of a tree to wait. Soon the sorceress approached, and the prince heard her call out,

Rapunzel, Rapunzel,
Let down your hair.

Rapunzel

Rapunzel let down her braids, and the sorceress climbed up the tower.

"So that's how it's done," said the prince. "Then I too will visit the songbird."

The following evening, the prince went to the foot of the tower and cried,

Rapunzel, Rapunzel,
Let down your hair.

As soon as she had let down her braids, the prince climbed up to her. At first Rapunzel was terribly frightened, for she had never seen a man before. But the prince spoke gently, and told her that her singing had touched his heart. Very soon Rapunzel forgot her fear, and when he asked her to marry him, she agreed at once. "Yes, I will gladly go with you, only it will take some work for me to get down out of the tower. Every night when you come, bring me a spool of silk thread. I will weave a strong ladder, and when it is finished I will climb down."

Rapunzel

The sorceress, of course, knew nothing of their plan, until one day, Rapunzel accidentally turned to her and said, "Why are you so much heavier than my prince? It takes no time at all for him to reach me. He always reaches me in a moment."

"Oh, you wicked child!" cried the sorceress. "I thought I had hidden you safely from the world, and yet you have managed to deceive me."

In her rage, she grabbed Rapunzel's beautiful hair, wound it around her wrist, and snipped it off with a pair of scissors. The sorceress then took Rapunzel to a deserted place, and left her to die.

That night, the sorceress fastened the braids to a hook on the tower window. The prince came and called out,

Rapunzel, Rapunzel,
Let down your hair.

The sorceress let down the braids, and the prince climbed up as usual. But instead of his dear Rapunzel, he found the sorceress, who screamed, "Aha! You thought you'd find your beloved, but the pretty bird is gone from this nest, and her song is done. The cat caught the bird, and will scratch your eyes out too."

The prince was beside himself with grief, and in his despair

Rapunzel

he jumped down from the tower. He escaped with his life, but the thorns he fell into pierced his eyes. Blind and miserable, he wandered through the forest for some years, as unhappy as he could be. At last he came to the deserted place where Rapunzel was living. Suddenly the prince heard a voice that lifted his heart up. He ran toward the sound, and when he was quite close, Rapunzel recognized him. Weeping, she ran to embrace him. Two of her tears touched his eyes, and in a moment he could see as well as ever. He led her to his kingdom, where they were received and welcomed with great joy. They had a beautiful wedding and they lived happily ever after. ✦

Nothing happens
unless first a dream.

—Carl Sandburg

TOUCH WOOD

All the children but the one dubbed "It" place themselves in various positions, each touching something that is wood. They then run from one wooden thing to another. "It" runs after them, and the first one he or she catches not touching wood becomes "It."

Rock, Paper, Scissors

Two players face each other. Each extends a closed fist and says "Rock, paper, scissors." At "scissors" they turn their fists into one of the three objects: rock (a closed fist), paper (an open palm), or scissors (two fingers in a V shape). A rock wins by crushing scissors, scissors wins by cutting paper, paper wins by covering rock. The child with the higher-ranked hand shape wins or gets a point.

Egg and Spoon Race

Each child holds a spoon by its handle and places a hard-boiled egg on the spoon. With the spoon in one hand and without touching the egg to steady it, each child races to the finish line. If a child drops the egg, he or she must get the egg, return to the spot where egg dropped and continue to the finish line. First one to reach the finish line is the winner.

The Peanut Song

Oh, a peanut sat
On a railroad track,

His heart was all a-flutter.

Along came the five-fifteen,

Uh-oh, peanut butter!

Round and Round

Round and round
The garden, like a
Teddy bear.

One step . . .

Two step . . .

And tickle under there!

Making Special Friends

Everybody needs a friend, and a little stuffed bear or doll often becomes an inseparable one for young children. Follow the steps below to make a beanbag bear or little girl doll. Your grandchildren will enjoy watching and helping their special friend come to life with a few snips and stitches. Substitute felt shapes for buttons and scraps of fabric for the beans if the doll is for a very young child.

BEANBAG BEAR OR DOLL

Scrap of felt or other fabric, needle, thread, buttons, yarn, dried beans

1. Fold your sheet of fabric in half and pin at the edges to hold.

2. Draw a teddy bear or gingerbread figure outline on the fabric and cut it out.

3. Sew two large buttons for eyes and a smaller button nose to the face on the front of one of your pieces of fabric. Stitch on a small piece of yarn for the mouth. A bear's mouth can be a little rounded W shape. A little girl's mouth can be heart-shaped. If you are not going to add clothing to your doll, sew two or three buttons onto the chest.

4. Let your grandchild name the doll. You can embroider the name (or your grandchild's name) on the back.

5. Place the two pieces of fabric together, front sides facing each other. Sew edges together, leaving a large opening for the beans. Take care to keep the stitches close together so that the dried beans won't slip out. If you are making a little girl with yarn hair, fold long pieces of yarn in half and place them between the two fabric pieces at the top of the head. Leave about 1/2 inch of yarn sticking out, and sew edges of fabric tight.

6. Turn the doll right side out. Stuff a generous amount of beans into the doll and sew the opening closed.

7. For a bear, make a little vest if you wish. For a girl doll, trim the front pieces of yarn shorter for bangs and make her a little dress, simple apron, or skirt.

If You're Happy

If you're hap-py and you know it, clap your hands.(clap, clap) If you're

hap-py and you know it, clap your hands. (clap, clap) If you're

hap-py and you know it, then your face will sure-ly show it. If you're

hap-py and you know it clap your hands. (clap, clap)

2. ...stomp your feet (stomp, stomp)...

3. ...shout hurray (Hurray!)...

4. ...do all three (clap, clap, stomp, stomp, hurray!)...

The Fisherman and His Wife

Once upon a time there was a fisherman who lived with his wife in a shack by the sea. One day he was sitting fishing by the clear water. Suddenly, he felt a big tug on his line, and when he pulled it up, there was a great fish on his hook. "Please let me live," the fish pleaded. "I am not really a fish. I am an enchanted prince."

"I want nothing to do with a fish that can talk," said the fisherman. "Swim away as fast as you please." So he put it back, and the fish darted straight down to the bottom.

When the fisherman returned home to his wife, he told her all about the great fish.

"Didn't you make a wish before letting him go?" asked his wife.

"No," said the fisherman. "What should I have wished for?"

"Ah!" said his wife. "We are so poor, living in this old, dirty shack. Go back and ask for a little cottage."

The fisherman did not like the idea of going, but he also did

The Fisherman and His Wife

not like arguing with his wife. When he got to the sea, the water
had turned yellowish green. He stood at the water's edge and said,

> Fishy, fishy in the sea,
> If you're a man, then speak to me.
> Though I don't like my wife's request,
> I've come to ask it nonetheless.

Then the great fish came swimming to him and asked, "What
does your wife desire?"

"Ah," said the fisherman, "my wife says that I should have
asked you for something before I let you go. She does not like living in a shack, and wants a little cottage."

"Go, then," said the fish. "It is done."

So the man went home to find his wife standing at the door of
a cozy cottage. "Come in, come in," she called.
"Isn't this better than the shack?" The rooms
were comfortable and clean, and behind the
cottage there was a little garden with all
sorts of flowers and fruit trees.

"Ah!" said the fisherman. "How happy
we shall be."

The Fisherman and His Wife

"We will try," said his wife.

Everything went well for about a week, and then the wife said, "Husband, this cottage is too cramped, and the garden is a great deal too small; I want to live in a large stone castle. Go to the fish again, and tell him to give us a castle."

"But Wife," said the fisherman, "I don't like to go to him again. We should be happy with the cottage."

"Nonsense!" said the wife. "It is easy for him to do. Go ask him."

The fisherman went, but his heart was very heavy. When he reached the sea, it looked dark purple and gloomy. He went close to it, and said,

> Fishy, fishy in the sea,
> If you're a man, then speak to me.
> Though I don't like my wife's request,
> I've come to ask it nonetheless.

"Well, what does she want now?" said the fish.

"Ah!" said the man, "My wife wants to live in a stone castle."

"Go home," said the fish. "It is done."

So the fisherman returned home and found his wife standing before a great castle. She took him by the hand as they entered.

The Fisherman and His Wife

The rooms were full of golden chairs and tables; and behind the castle was a wooded area half a mile long, full of sheep, and goats, and hares, and deer; and in the courtyard were stables for horses and cows and the finest carriages. "Well," said the fisherman, "now we will live contented and happy in this beautiful castle for the rest of our lives."

"Perhaps," said the wife. "But let us consider and sleep on it before we make up our minds." So they went to bed.

The next morning, the wife woke up at daybreak and saw the glorious countryside through her window. Her husband yawned, so she poked him with her elbow. "Get up, Husband," she said. "We must rule over all the land. I want us to be king and queen."

"Wife, Wife," said the fisherman, "why should I wish to be king? I will not be king."

"Husband," she said, "say no more about it, just go and try. I shall be queen!" So the man went away, but he was nervous. The sea looked a dark gray, and was covered with foam as he cried out,

Fishy, fishy in the sea,
If you're a man, then speak to me.
Though I don't like my wife's request,
I've come to ask it nonetheless.

162

The Fisherman and His Wife

"Well, what does she want now?" said the fish.

"Great fish," said the fisherman, "my wife wants us to be king and queen."

"Go home," said the fish. "It is done."

Then the fisherman went home. As he came close to the palace, he saw a troop of soldiers and heard the sound of drums and trumpets. When he entered, he saw his wife sitting on a high throne of gold and diamonds, with a golden crown upon her head. "Ah, Wife!" said the fisherman. "What a fine thing it is to be king and queen! Now we shall never have anything more to wish for."

"I don't know about that," she said. "Never is a long time. I am queen, it's true, but I should be pope. Go to the fish, and ask him to make me pope."

"Oh, Wife, Wife!" he said, "How can you be pope? There is but one pope at a time in Christendom. The fish cannot make you pope."

"What nonsense!" she said, "If he can make a king, he can make a pope. Go and try him."

So the fisherman went. But when he came to the shore the wind and sea were raging, and the ships danced upon the haz-

The Fisherman and His Wife

ardous waves. The fisherman was terribly frightened, and trembled, so that his knees knocked together. But he went to the shore and said,

> Fishy, fishy in the sea,
> If you're a man, then speak to me.
> Though I don't like my wife's request,
> I've come to ask it nonetheless.

"What does she want now?" said the fish.

"Ah!" said the fisherman. "She wants to be pope."

"Go home," said the fish. "It is done."

Then the fisherman went home and found his wife sitting on a throne that was two miles high; and she had three great crowns on her head. Many bishops and priests stood around her, and on either side there were two rows of burning lights of all sizes. "Well, Wife," said the fisherman, "it is a grand thing to be pope; and now you must be content, for you can be nothing greater."

"We'll see," said the wife. Then they went to bed, but the fisherman's wife could not sleep all night for thinking what she should be next. At last morning came and the sun rose. "Ha!" she

The Fisherman and His Wife

whispered as she looked through the window. "I must have the power to rule the sun!" She woke her husband, and said, "Husband, go to the fish and tell him I want to be Lord of the sun and moon." The fisherman was half asleep, but the thought terrified him so much that he fell out of bed.

"Oh, Wife!" he said, "isn't being pope enough?"

"No," she said, "I am very uneasy, and cannot bear to see the sun and moon rise without my permission. Go to the fish quickly."

The fisherman was trembling with fear; and as he was going down to the shore a dreadful storm arose, so that the trees and the rocks shook; and the heavens became black, and the lightning struck, and the thunder rolled; and the fisherman said,

> Fishy, fishy in the sea,
> If you're a man, then speak to me.
> Though I don't like my wife's request,
> I've come to ask it nonetheless.

"What does she want now?" said the fish.

"Ah!" said the fisherman. "She wants to be Lord of the sun and moon."

"Go home," said the fish, "to your shack again!"

And there they live in their old, dirty shack to this very day. ✦

Little Red Riding Hood

Put on a puppet show of this favorite fairy tale with your grandchildren! (Parents can be the audience.) The puppets can be as elaborate as you and your grandchildren wish. You can substitute plastic spoons, permanent markers, glue, and felt in place of painting and sewing to simplify the spoon puppets. Alternatively, give Red a paper basket or dress up Grandma in lace, ribbons, and notions.

The script that follows can be simplified or added to. If there is only one little puppeteer, let him or her decide whether to be the Wolf or Red. You will easily be able to play all the other short parts. For young children, it may be enough to use just the two puppets and enact the scene between Red Riding Hood and the Wolf at Grandma's house. Good luck!

SPOON PUPPETS

Acrylic paints, paintbrush; two large wooden spoons; one small wooden spoon; colored yarn; glue; scissors; red, white, and green cloth; needle, thread

1. Paint Little Red Riding Hood's face onto the backside of the smaller wooden spoon. Paint Grandma's face with glasses and Hunter's face with mustache on the two larger spoons. (You can use plastic spoons and permanent markers instead.) Glue on different colored yarns for hair.

2. Cut three cloth circles about twice the length of the spoon handles: a smaller red circle for Red, white for Grandma, and green for Hunter. Cut a small hole in the middle of each circle. Slip each spoon handle through the appropriate-colored cloth. Use tape to fasten the underside of each cloth to its handle. (For Red, make and attach hood described in step 3 before completing step 2.)

3. Red's Hood: put two small pieces of red cloth on top of each other. Cut out a *D* shape slighter taller than the length of Red's spoon head. Sew together about 2/3 of the curve of the *D* (the

bottom of the curve and the straight edge remain separate). Insert the bottom of *D* into the small circle in the middle of Red's cape. Open the hood's two bottom pieces and sew onto the underside of the cape.

4. Grandma's Cap: Cut a white circle about twice the width of Grandma's spoon head. Place some leftover fabric in the center of the circle and gather up the edge to form a pouch. Wrap a rubber band once or twice around it, just tight enough to hold in the stuffing but loose enough to fit around the top portion of Grandma's spoon head (you can use a ribbon to cover up the rubber band if you wish). Fluff out the frilly edge of Grandma's cap and adjust on Grandma's head. You will need to remove Grandma's cap and tape it onto the Wolf's head in the middle of the play. The little cap will look ridiculous on the Wolf, but that's part of the fun!

5. Hold spoon handles to move puppets. If you wish, cut two slits in the front and center of each cloth cape. The thumb and index fingers of your hand can go through the slits to become moveable puppet hands.

THE BIG, BAD WOLF

Brown sock, scissors, white felt, two white buttons (optional), glue, black felt or black button, brown felt, black or brown yarn

1. Pull the sock over your hand. Thrust your thumb into the heel section and your fingers into the toe section to form a mouth. Note where you will add teeth, eyes (where your knuckles are), nose, ears, and tail.

2. Cut triangular pieces of white felt for the big, bad wolf's sharp teeth—glue these to the edges of the mouth.

3. Glue or sew on white felt or white button eyes and a black felt or black button nose.

4. Glue on two large, brown felt triangles for ears; tufts of brown yarn for hair, and a long yarn tail.

Putting on the Show

NARRATOR
Once upon a time there was a lovely girl who wore her favorite hooded cape everywhere she went. Her nickname was Little Red Riding Hood, but sometimes "Red" for short. One sunny afternoon, Little Red Riding Hood's mother sent her to take a "get well" basket of chicken soup and crackers to her grandmother, who had a terrible cold. Her grandmother lived not far away, in a little cabin in the woods.

RED
I'm Little Red Riding Hood and I'm on my way to Grandma's house. Mom says I should go right to Grandma's house and not talk to strangers. And so here I go into the woods! (*Red skips through the woods and then stops suddenly.*)

RED
Oh! Look at those beautiful raspberries over there. I'll just stop for a little bit and pick some for Grandma.

WOLF (*in sweet voice*)
H-e-l-l-l-o-o, little girl!

RED
Oops! You scared me! I dropped all my raspberries!

WOLF
May I help you pick them up?

RED
Well, you look like a nice wolf, but I'm not allowed to talk to strangers.

WOLF
So I will just help and not talk to you.

RED
Oh, that's a good idea. (*They pick up berries for a while.*)

WOLF (*yawning*)
My, it's getting late! It's almost my bedtime.

RED
Oh no! I'm very late getting to Grandma's house. It's going to get dark soon! What am I going to do?

WOLF
Well, little girl, why don't you go this way? It's a shortcut.

RED
Thanks! (*Red goes off, but the shortcut is actually very long. The wolf tricked Red so he could get to Grandma's house first!*)

WOLF
Knock Knock!

GRANDMA

Who's there?

WOLF (*sweet tiny voice*)

It's Little Red Riding Hood!

GRANDMA

Come in, I've been waiting for you . . . ! AHHHH! A wolf!!

WOLF

Grrrrrr! Get over here! Get into the closet. I'll eat you after I take care of Little Red Riding Hood! And be quiet! Otherwise I'll eat you both nice and slowly instead of in one big bite! Oh, give me your cap! (*Wolf puts on Grandma's cap and jumps into bed. Little Red Riding Hood soon arrives.*)

RED

Granny, it's me, Little Red Riding Hood. I've brought you some soup and fresh berries to make you feel better.

WOLF

Come closer, so I can see you, child! You know how bad my eyes are.

RED

Granny, what big eyes you have!

WOLF

The better to see you with, dear. Now come closer.

RED

Granny, what big ears you have!

WOLF

The better to smell you with. Come just a bit closer, dear.

RED

Oh Granny! What a BIG mouth you have!

WOLF

Grrr! Yes! The better to EAT YOU WITH!!!

RED

AAHHHHH! (*Wolf chases Red around.*)

RED

Help! Help! Help! (*A hunter who has been out in the woods nearby hears the screams and rushes to the cabin.*)

HUNTER

What's happening? Oh my! A wolf! *BANG!* (*A very young child can be responsible for this single exciting sound effect.*)

RED

Oh, thank you, thank you, thank you! But where is my grandmother?

GRANDMA

Here I am! Let me out of here!

RED

Oh, Grandma! I'm so happy to see you! I promise I will never ever talk to strangers again. . . especially big, bad wolf strangers!

THE END

Girls

and Boys

Girls and boys come out to play,
The moon doth shine as bright as day,
Leave your supper and leave your sleep,
And come with your playfellows into the street.

Come with a whoop, come with a call,
Come with a good will, or come not at all.

Up the ladder and down the wall,
A halfpenny bun will serve us all.
You find milk and I'll find flour.
And we'll have pudding in half an hour.

Blueberry Corn Muffins

Breakfast at Grandmother's house is special. Gently wake up your grandchildren with the aroma of baking muffins. What a wonderful way to greet the morning! Serve these warm with homemade jams *(page 71)*, sit back, and enjoy the sight of your little ones' blueberry- and jam-smeared faces.

1 1/2 cups yellow cornmeal
1 1/2 cups sifted white flour
3/4 cup white sugar
4 1/2 teaspoons baking powder
1 teaspoon salt
3 teaspoons butter, softened
3 eggs
1 1/2 cups milk
1 cup blueberries

1. Preheat the oven to 425°F.

2. In a large bowl, combine dry ingredients and cut in butter.

3. In a separate bowl, beat together the eggs and then beat in the milk. Add to the dry ingredients and mix well.

4. Stir in blueberries.

5. Spoon batter into greased muffin pans. Bake 15 to 20 minutes, until tops are golden brown and an inserted fork comes out clean.

Makes twelve to sixteen large muffins.

Billy Boy

Oh, ___ where have you been, Bil - ly Boy, Bil - ly boy, Oh, ___

where have you been, charm-ing Bil - ly? ___ I have

been to seek a wife, She's the joy ___ of my life, She's a

young thing and can - not leave her moth - er. ___ I have

2. Did she ask you to come in, Billy Boy,
 Billy Boy,
Did she ask you to come in, charming Billy?
Yes, she asked me to come in, there's a
 dimple in her chin,
She's a young thing and cannot leave her
 mother.

3. Can she make a cherry pie, Billy Boy...
She can make a cherry pie, quick as a cat
 can wink an eye...

4. How old is she, Billy Boy...
Three times six and four times seven,
 twenty-eight and eleven...

MUSICAL CHAIRS

Someone needs to control the music. Chairs are placed in two rows, back to back, one less in number than the players, who then gallop round them in time to the music. Suddenly the music stops, and everybody tries to sit in a chair. Whoever doesn't get a chair is then out of the game. A chair is removed and the game continues until only one player, the winner, is left.

LONDON BRIDGE

Two children clasp hands and raise them to form an arch or "bridge." The rest of the players walk under the bridge one by one, singing:

> London Bridge is falling down, falling down, falling down.
> London Bridge is falling down, my fair lady!

When they sing "my fair lady," the bridge drops and traps someone in their arms. They begin rocking the trapped child in their arms singing:

> Take a key and lock her up, lock her up, lock her up.
> Take a key and lock her up, my fair lady!

The trapped child then replaces one of the children forming the bridge and the game continues.

BLIND MAN'S BUFF

One child is blindfolded with a handkerchief so that he or she cannot see, and is placed in the middle of a small, fairly empty room. The other children turn her around three times, and she tries to catch anyone she can. The other children need to call out to help her. The one caught has to be the next "blind man."

Learn to enjoy the little things—
there are so many of them.

—Anonymous

Lemon Squares

The next time you serve up a snack for your grandchildren, try some of these zesty lemon tarts. With a perfectly textured crust and creamy filling, they are fabulous!

CRUST

3$^{1}/_{2}$ cups all-purpose white flour
$^{1}/_{4}$ cup confectioners' sugar
$^{1}/_{4}$ teaspoon salt
28 tablespoons (3$^{1}/_{2}$ sticks) unsalted butter, cut into bits

1. Preheat the oven to 350°F.

2. In a large bowl, sift together the flour, sugar, and salt. With a pastry blender or two knives, cut the butter into the flour mixture until it has the consistency of cornmeal.

3. Press the dough onto a large baking sheet (10" x 15", with 2-inch-high sides).

4. Bake for 20 minutes.

FILLING

6 large eggs
3 cups granulated sugar
2 tablespoons grated lemon zest
$^{3}/_{4}$ cup lemon juice
$^{2}/_{3}$ cup all-purpose white flour
1 teaspoon baking powder
Confectioners' sugar for dusting

1. While the crust is baking, beat the eggs until blended and then beat in the following ingredients slowly, in this order: sugar, lemon zest, lemon juice, flour and baking powder. Blend until smooth.

2. Pour the mixture over the crust and bake for 25 more minutes.

3. Cool in the pan set up on a rack. Using a sharp knife, carefully cut into squares and dust with confectioners' sugar.

Makes about thirty-six 2-inch squares.

Chocolate Fudge

Chocolate fudge is the stuff of sweet dreams! Imagine your grandchildren with a light dusting of sugar on their faces and syrup dripping off their fingers on a lazy Sunday afternoon. The smell of chocolate and the sound of laughter fill the air. All wait impatiently for the fudge to cool—and then, a taste of heaven.

18 ounces (2 3/4 cups) semi-sweet chocolate chips
8 ounces (4 cups) mini marshmallows
2 sticks of unsweetened butter, melted
1 tablespoon vanilla
2 cups chopped walnuts (optional)
4 1/2 cups white sugar
1 12—ounce can evaporated milk

1. Butter a nine-by-thirteen-inch dish. Set aside.

2. In a mixing bowl, combine chocolate, marshmallows, butter, vanilla and walnuts (don't worry that the maxture isn't really melding together). Set aside.

3. In a large pot stir together sugar and evaporated milk. Bring to a rolling boil and stir constantly for 10 minutes (a long-handled wooden spoon works best).

4. Turn off heat and add contents of the bowl to the pot.
Stir rapidly until everything is melted and fudge is smooth.

5. Pour into buttered dish and chill briefly (about an hour) to harden.
Remove from fridge and let stand until fudge reached room temperature, then cut into 1-inch squares.

Makes about one hundred 1-inch squares.

The Shower
by Catherine A. Morin

One day, as they all scampered home from
    their school, the Pixies—*and* Polly,
It started to rain, and poor Polly—oh, dear!—
    had forgotten her brolly!

"Hooray!" cried the Pixies, "*we* don't need
    umbrellas; ho! isn't this jolly!"
Each crept 'neath a stool, leaving Polly in the rain
    feeling quite melancholy.

R

Thirty days hath September,
April, June, and November.
February has twenty-eight alone,
All the rest have thirty-one;
Excepting leap-year,
That's the time
When February's days are twenty-nine.

Months

Oats, Peas, Beans and Barley Grow

Oats, peas, beans and bar - ley grow; Oats, peas, beans and bar - ley grow; Do you or I, or an - y - one know how oats, peas, beans and bar - ley grow?

2. First the farmer sows his seed,
   Then he stands and takes his ease;
   He stamps his foot and claps his hands,
   and turns around to view the land.

3. Waiting for a partner,
   Waiting for a partner,
   Open the ring and take one in
   While we all gaily dance and sing.

186

·Hilda Austin·

Delores's Sunday Special

My stepson, Jay, grew up with his Grandmother Delores's chicken wings and zucchini tomato pie. I couldn't get him to choose one over the other and so share both. You can serve them together.

HONEY GLAZED CHICKEN WINGS

3 lbs. chicken wings
1 teaspoon salt
1/2 teaspoon pepper
2 tablespoons vegetable oil
1/2 cup honey
1/4 cup soy sauce
1 large can plum tomatoes, crushed
1 clove garlic, minced
2 tablespoons ketchup

1. Preheat oven to 375°F.
2. Put the chicken wings in a shallow pan and sprinkle with salt and pepper.
3. Mix remaining ingredients and pour over wings.
4. Bake 1 hour or until wings are brown.
5. Serve immediately.

Serves four to six.

ZUCCHINI TOMATO PIE

2 cups chopped zucchini
1 cup chopped tomato
1/2 cup chopped onion
1/3 cup grated Parmesan cheese
1 1/2 cups milk
3/4 cup Bisquik
3 eggs
1/2 teaspoon salt
1/4 teaspoon pepper

1. Preheat oven to 400°F.
2. Grease a 10-inch pie pan and sprinkle the vegetables into the pan.
3. Beat the remaining ingredients until smooth (about 15 seconds in a blender or 1 minute with a handheld mixer) and then pour over vegetables.
4. Bake approximately 30 minutes, or until an inserted knife comes out clean.

Serves four to six.

Vegetarian Lasagna

This is a great dish to prepare ahead of time before the family arrives. Simply put it into the oven an hour before dinner and then sit down to make the most of your time with your loved ones. Add a simple salad and some bread, and your meal is complete.

1 lb. lasagna noodles
2 tablespoons olive oil
10 ounces ricotta cheese (part skim or
    nonfat ricotta may be substituted)
1 cup pesto sauce
6 cups raw spinach, rinsed and chopped
4 to 5 cups tomato sauce
1 cup tomato paste
3 cups shredded mozzarella cheese
    (part skim or nonfat mozzarella
    may be substituted)

1. Preheat oven to 350°F.

2. In a large stockpot, bring 6 to 8 cups water to a boil. Add pasta and oil; let cook approximately 8 minutes.

3. While pasta cooks, mix ricotta cheese, pesto sauce, and spinach in a large bowl. Set aside.

4. In a large saucepan, heat tomato sauce and tomato paste, stirring until blended. Turn off heat and set aside.

5. Drain pasta and begin assembly. In a 13- x 9-inch baking dish, spread, in order, a thin layer of sauce, pasta, 1/2 ricotta mixture, sauce, pasta, sauce, 1 cup mozzarella, pasta, 1/2 ricotta mixture, sauce, pasta, sauce, 1 cup mozzarella, pasta, and sauce. Finally, top with remaining mozzarella.

6. Cover with aluminum foil and bake approximately 45 minutes. Remove foil and bake another 10 minutes. Let lasagna stand for at least 10 minutes before serving.

Serves eight to ten.

Try, Try Again

by T. H. Palmer

'Tis a lesson you should heed,
   Try, try again;
If at first you don't succeed,
   Try, try again;
Then your courage should appear,
For, if you will persevere,
You will conquer, never fear;
   Try, try again.

Little Cabin in The Wood

Lit - tle ca - bin in the wood, Lit - tle man by the win - dow stood,

Lit - tle rab - bit hop - ping by, knock - ing at the door.

"Help me! Help me, sir!" he said, 'fore the farm - er bops my head.

"Come on in," the lit - tle man cried, "Warm up by the fire."

Little cabin
In the wood,

Little man by the
Window stood,

Little rabbit
Hopping by,

Knocking
At the door.

"Help me! Help me, sir!"
He said, "'fore the farmer...

... Bops my
Head."

"Come on in,"
The little man cried,

"Warm up by the fire."

Grandmother Says...

There is a time and a place for everything.

>—+—◆—⊙—◆+—<

Early to bed and early to rise, make a man healthy, wealthy, and wise.

>—+—◆—⊙—◆+—<

Two heads are better than one.

>—+—◆—⊙—◆+—<

If a job's worth doing, it's worth doing well.

>—+—◆—⊙—◆+—<

Necessity is the mother of invention.

>—+—◆—⊙—◆+—<

A rolling stone gathers
no moss.

Time and tide wait
for no man.

Time cures all things.

Tomorrow is another day.

Many hands make light work.

There's no place like home.

An apple a day keeps the doctor away.

Pretty (and Yummy) Things

*T*each your grandchildren about the joy of giving. Encourage them to make two friendship bracelets—one to keep and one to give. Granddaughters will love the felt flower chain, which can be adapted to make a necklace, bracelet, or belt. And the sweet necklace is so yummy, even grandsons will enjoy making one (or two) to snack on.

FELT FLOWER CHAIN

marker, felt, scissors, stapler, glue, long strip of ribbon

1. Draw simple flower shapes onto felt and cut out. Flowers should be at least an inch wide.

2. Cut out centers for the flowers from the leftover scraps—they can be simple circles, stars, or smaller flower shapes. Shapes should be about $1/2$ inch wide.

3. Staple flowers onto the ribbon, keeping the ends of the staples on the flower side.

4. Glue the flower centers onto the flowers, covering the staple ends. (If you wish to make smaller flowers with smaller centers, use needle and thread to stitch onto ribbon instead of stapling.)

FRIENDSHIP BRACELET

$1 1/2$ feet suede cord, three beads, scissors

1. Cut the cord into three 2-inch pieces and two 6-inch pieces.

2. Use one 6-inch piece to tie together the three short pieces.

3. Braid together the three short pieces for a bit, slide a bead onto the middle lace, and repeat with remaining cord and two beads.

4. Tie off with remaining 6-inch cord. Approximate the length required to tie around little wrists and trim off excess.

SWEET JEWELRY

Cheerios, Fruit Loops, Apple Jacks cereal, long licorice strips

1. String the cereal onto the licorice. Tie the ends together, wear, and eat!

Cookies and Treats

How does that cookie jar empty so fast? Well, it certainly can't be left that way! Keep baking these treats with care, and your grandchildren will never eat a cookie in their lives without reminiscing about their childhood in Granny's kitchen.

CINNAMON SUGAR COOKIES

1/2 cup butter (1 stick), room temperature

1/2 teaspoon salt

1 teaspoon grated lemon rind

1 1/4 cups sugar

2 eggs

2 tablespoons milk

2 cups flour

1 teaspoon baking powder

1/2 teaspoon baking soda

2 tablespoons ground cinnamon

1. Preheat oven to 400°F.
2. In a large mixing bowl, cream together butter, salt, lemon rind, and 1 cup sugar.
3. Add eggs and milk. Mix well.
4. In a separate bowl, combine flour, baking powder, and baking soda, and gradually add to the above mixture. Mix well.
5. Drop mixture onto greased cookie sheet, one rounded tablespoon at a time, 2 inches apart.
6. In a small bowl, mix 1/4 cup sugar and cinnamon.
7. Butter the bottom of a glass, dip into the cinnamon sugar mixture and flatten one cookie. Repeat until all cookies are flattened.
8. Bake 8 to 10 minutes until light golden.
9. Transfer cookies to wire racks and let cool.

Makes two and a half dozen cookies.

CHOCOLATE-CHIP COOKIES

5 1/3 tablespoons butter,
     room temperature
1/2 cup sugar
1/4 cup packed brown sugar
1 egg
1 teaspoon vanilla extract
1 cup flour
1/2 teaspoon baking soda
1/2 teaspoon salt
1 cup semisweet chocolate chips

1. Preheat oven to 375°F.
2. In a large mixing bowl, cream together butter, white sugar, and brown sugar until light.
3. Add egg and vanilla. Mix well.
4. In a separate bowl, combine flour, baking soda, and salt, and gradually add to the above mixture. Mix well.
5. Add chocolate chips and mix well.
6. Drop mixture onto greased cookie sheet, one rounded tablespoon at a time, around 2 inches apart. (If using cookies for ice-cream sandwiches *(page 34)*, flatten dough slightly with back of spoon.) Bake 8 to 10 minutes until golden brown.
7. Transfer cookies to wire racks and let cool.

Makes about two dozen cookies.

MARSHMALLOW RICE TREATS

3 tablespoons unsalted butter
10 ounces mini-marshmallows
6 cups toasted rice cereal
1/2 cup chopped dried cranberries
1/2 cup chopped dried apricots

1. In a large stockpot, melt butter and marshmallows together.
2. Turn off heat and stir in cereal and dried fruits.
3. Spoon onto a 9" x 11" baking pan lined with wax paper. Flatten out using another piece of wax paper on top.
4. When cool, slice into 2-inch squares and store in sealed container.

Makes about two dozen treats.

Good ... Children
by Robert Louis Stevenson

Children, you are very little,
And your bones are very brittle;
If you would grow great and stately,
You must try to walk sedately.

You must still be bright and quiet,
And content with simple diet;
And remain, through all bewild'ring,
Innocent and honest children.

Happy hearts and happy faces,
Happy play in grassy places—
That was how, in ancient ages,
Children grew to kings and sages.

Twelve Dancing Princesses

Once upon a time there was a king who had twelve beautiful daughters. The princesses slept side by side in twelve beds. Each night when they went to bed, the king shut and locked their door. But each morning he opened the door to find that their shoes had been danced to pieces, and nobody could explain how it happened.

So the king announced that anyone who discovered where the princesses secretly danced in the night could choose one of them to be his wife and would inherit the kingdom. But whoever tried and failed to make the discovery after three days and nights would be put to death.

A prince soon appeared and offered to take the risk. At night, he was taken to the chamber next to the one where the princesses slept in their twelve beds. The doors of both chambers were left open so that the princesses could not leave without being seen. But the prince's eyes grew heavy, and he fell asleep on his watch.

Twelve Dancing Princesses

When he woke in the morning, all the princesses had been dancing. The soles of their shoes were full of holes. The second and third evenings passed with the same result, and the prince lost his head. Many others came after him and offered to take the chance, but they all lost their lives.

One day, an old soldier passed through the kingdom. On his travels he met an old woman who asked him where he was going. "I hardly know myself," said the soldier, and added jokingly, "I'd like to discover where the twelve princesses dance, and become king."

"Well, that's not very hard to do," said the old woman. "Don't drink any of the wine the princesses serve in the evening. Then, as soon as they leave you, pretend to be fast asleep."

The old woman gave him a cloak and said, "When you wear this, you will be invisible. Follow the princesses wherever they go." Once the soldier heard all this good advice, he was determined to try his luck.

He was welcomed into the castle, and when the evening came he was led to the outer chamber. Just as he was going to lie down, the eldest of the princesses brought him a cup of

Twelve Dancing Princesses

wine. The soldier had tied a sponge beneath his chin, and he let the wine run into it. He didn't drink a drop. Then he lay down on his bed, and in a little while began to snore very loudly. When the twelve princesses heard this they laughed, and the eldest said, "This fellow, too, might have done better things with his life!" They groomed themselves in front of their mirrors, and skipped about, eager to begin dancing.

Sure that they were quite safe, the eldest went up to her own bed and clapped her hands, and the bed sunk into the floor. The soldier saw them going down through the opening one after another, the eldest leading the way. With no time to lose, he jumped up, put on the invisible cloak, and followed them. But in the middle of the stairs he stepped on the corner of the youngest princess's dress, causing her to cry out to her sisters, "Someone grabbed at my dress."

"You silly creature!" said the eldest. "You caught it on a nail." Then down they all went, and at the bottom they found themselves in a most delightful orchard. The leaves on the trees were silver, and glittered and sparkled. The soldier wished to take away some token of the place; so he broke off a little branch. Snap!

"Did you hear that noise?" asked the youngest sister. "Something is terribly wrong."

Twelve Dancing Princesses

"It is only our princes, who are shouting for joy at our approach," said the eldest.

Then they came to another orchard, where all the leaves on the trees were gold; and afterward to a third, where the leaves were all glittering diamonds. The soldier broke a branch from each; and every time there was a loud noise, which made the youngest sister tremble with fear. Snap! Crack! But the eldest still said it was only the princes, who were crying for joy. So they went on until they came to a great lake; and at the side of the lake were twelve little boats with twelve handsome princes in them.

The princesses got into their boats, and the soldier stepped into the same boat with the youngest. As they were rowing over the lake, her prince said, "I don't understand it, but the boat seems much heavier today.

"It is only the heavy heat," said the princess.

On the other side of the lake stood a beautiful, brightly lit palace. When the boats landed, everyone rushed up the palace steps. Each prince danced with his princess, and the invisible soldier danced among them; and when any of the princesses had a cup of wine set by her, he drank it all up, so that when she put the cup to her mouth it was empty. At this, too, the youngest sister was

Twelve Dancing Princesses

horribly frightened, but the eldest always silenced her. They danced until three o'clock in the morning, and then all their shoes were worn out. So, the princes rowed them back over the lake; but this time the soldier placed himself in the boat with the eldest princess. On the opposite shore, the princesses said good-bye to their princes.

As they approached the staircase, the soldier quickly ran ahead to his room and lay down. The sisters heard the soldier snoring in his bed. They said, "We are safe." In the morning, the soldier said nothing about what had happened. He wanted to see more of this strange adventure, and went again the second and third nights. Everything happened just as before; however, on the third night,

Twelve Dancing Princesses

the soldier carried away one of the golden cups as a token of where he had been.

Finally, the soldier was taken before the king to tell what he knew. He brought the three branches and the golden cup. The king asked him where his twelve daughters danced at night. The soldier told the king all that had happened and showed him the three branches and the golden cup. The king called for the princesses, and asked them if what the soldier said was true. They confessed, and the king asked the soldier which daughter he would choose for his wife. He answered, "I am not very young, so I will have the eldest."

They were married that very day, and the soldier was chosen to be the king's successor. ◆

Lenore's Chicken Potpie

Leonore is a grandmother with two recipes in this book and, if the truth be told, she probably should have her own cookbook altogether. She simply never makes anything that isn't high-end comfort food. Her chicken potpie is superb. She does make her own dough; however, to simplify life, I recommend you buy it frozen.

4 cups chicken broth
3 poached and cubed chicken breasts
4 to 5 cups cubed vegetables (any mixture of carrots, leeks, celery, mushrooms, pearl onions, zucchini, corn, green peas)
3 tablespoons butter
4 tablespoons flour
1 cup heavy cream
Salt and pepper to taste
9 oz. pastry dough
A little white flour for rolling out dough
1 egg

1. Preheat oven to 400°F.
2. Boil the chicken broth until it is reduced by half. Set aside.
3. Mix chicken and fresh vegetables and put in a baking dish.
4. Melt butter in a saucepan, add flour, and cook, whisking over medium-low heat, 2 to 3 minutes. Add broth. Cook, whisking, until thickened, another 3 to 4 minutes. Salt and pepper to taste and pour over chicken and vegetables.
5. On a lightly floured surface, roll the pastry out to form the shape of your baking dish, adding 1 1/2" for an overlap.
6. Whisk egg. Brush the outside rim of baking dish with egg. Lay the pastry on top of dish and crimp around the edges. Use a fork to tamp down the edges, giving it a decorative look. Brush egg over the crust. Make a few small cuts in the crust for the steam to escape.
7. Bake for 20 minutes. Reduce heat to 375°F and bake another 15 to 20 minutes.

Serves four.

Boom, Boom, Ain't It Great to be Crazy

A horse and a flea and three blind mice

Sat on a curb-stone shoot-ing dice, The

horse he slipped and fell on the flea,

"Whoops," said the flea, "There's a horse on me!"

Chorus

Boom, boom, ain't it great to be cra - zy, Boom,

boom, ain't it great to be cra - zy,

Gid - dy and fool - ish the whole day through, Boom,

boom, ain't it great to be cra - zy?

2. Way down South where bananas grow,
A flea stepped on an elephant's toe,
The elephant cried with tears in his eyes,
"Why don't you pick on someone your size?"

Chorus

3. Way up North where there's ice and snow,
There lived a penguin and his name was Joe,
He got so tired of black and white,
He wore pink slacks to the dance last night.

Chorus

Old Mother

Old Mother Hubbard
Went to the cupboard,
To give her poor dog a bone;
But when she got there
The cupboard was bare,
And so the poor dog had none.

Hubbard

Advice to
Small Children

by Edward Anthony

Eat no green apples
    or you'll droop,
Be careful not
    to get the croup,
Avoid the chicken-pox
    and such,
And don't fall out
    of windows much.

Momma Bread

My high-school girlfriend, Pleasant Coggershall, baked the best bread I ever had. My own children yearned for it ever since they tasted it, and so I've made it every Thanksgiving for many years. I make enough to freeze, give away, toast for breakfast, and make sandwiches with stuffing, turkey, lingonberries, and gravy the day after Thanksgiving. Yum.

4 cups lukewarm water
1 tablespoon sugar
3 packages active dry yeast
3/4 lb. (3 sticks) butter, melted
3 tablespoons kosher salt
1/2 cup honey
1/4 to 1/2 cup of molasses
5 eggs (room temperature)
3 lbs. whole wheat flour (9 cups)
2 lbs. unbleached white flour (6 cups)

1. Empty yeast into 2 cups of water in a large bowl and add sugar. Set aside in a warmish place for 15 to 20 minutes, until foamy.
2. Add, in the following order—stirring as you go—butter, salt, honey, molasses, eggs, 2 cups of water, and the whole-wheat flour. Mix.
3. Add the white flour (reserving about 1 cup for kneading), and mix again. Let stand for 10 minutes.
4. Transfer the dough to a lightly floured surface and knead at least 10 to 15 minutes. If the dough is sticky, sprinkle it lightly with flour as you work.
5. Butter a large bowl. Turn the dough in the butter to coat. Cover loosely with a warm, damp dishtowel and set aside in a warmish place to rise for 1 1/2 to 2 hours. Punch it down and let it rise again (1/2 hour or so.)
6. Preheat oven to 450°F. Butter five 9" x 5" x 3" loaf pans or two cookie trays.
7. Transfer the dough to a lightly floured surface. Cut into five pieces. Knead each, shaping it into a loaf. Press loaves into prepared pans or put on trays. Cover again and let them rise 1/2 hour.
8. Bake all the loaves together at 450°F for 10 minutes. Turn heat down to 350°F. Bake until bread is golden brown (another 20 to 30 minutes). Remove loaves from pans and let cool.

Makes five loaves.

This is My Wish for You

by Charles Livingston Snell

This is my wish for you …

That the spirit of beauty may continually hover about you and fold you close within the tendernesses of her wings.

That each beautiful and gracious thing in life may be unto you as a symbol of good for your soul's delight.

That sun-glories and star-glories, leaf-glories and bark-glories, flower-glories and glories that lurk in the grasses of the field; glories of mountains and oceans of little streams of running waters; glories of song, of poesy, of all the arts may be to you as sweet, abiding influences that will illumine your life and make you glad.

That your soul may be as an alabaster cup, filled to overflowing with the mystical wine of beauty and love.

That happiness may put her arms around you, and wisdom make your soul serene.

This is my wish for you.

Sleep, Baby, Sleep

Sleep, baby, sleep,
Our cottage vale is deep:
The little lamb is on the green,
With woolly fleece so soft and clean—
    Sleep, baby, sleep.

Sleep, baby, sleep,
Down where the woodbines creep;
Be always like the lamb so mild,
A kind, and sweet, and gentle child.
    Sleep, baby, sleep.